2/-

D1422772

# DZOKUTI IN THE BUSH

# Dzokuti In The Bush

*by*
URSULA d'IVRY

*With illustrations
by the author*

*London: Peter Davies*

Copyright © by Ursula d'Ivry Russell 1959

FIRST PUBLISHED 1959


PRINTED AND BOUND IN GREAT BRITAIN FOR PETER DAVIES LTD.
BY NOVELLO & CO. LTD., LONDON AND SLOUGH

TO ROLAND

' *I loafe and invite my soul,*
  *I lean and loafe at my ease observing a spear of*
    *summer grass.*'

WALT WHITMAN

All the characters found in this book
    Are completely
    And utterly
    Fictitious,
    Invented solely to amuse.

All the characters found in this book
    Will be found
    In Africa, England, Australia . . .
    Where people
    Are found
    If anyone cares to look.

*Dzokuti*—Shona word meaning "talk nonsense"

## CHAPTER ONE

THE Southern Cross sparkled on the horizon, recumbent, and the topaz African moon had long since retired. Outside, frogs were loud, some with baritone croaks, some with apologetic creaks, and others with the liquid and abruptly terminating plop of a bursting bubble as they sang a ballad of love in the dark—or, one could say, they made a deafening racket; it depends on the way one feels about things. A man closed the window and the frog chorus was supplanted by the clink of glasses and explosions of affected laughter—sounds that collided and splintered in a steady percussion throughout the room.

The deceleration of the party was apparent in the overflowing ashtrays when I was introduced to somebody's aunt, and thought "How boring!" With her soft complexion and vigorous, boy-cut hair she had reached her middle forties without mishap to her features; apart from deepening lines at the corners of her twinkling eyes, and an added contour to her squarely humorous jaw, it was apparent that a further ten years would see little change.

Summoning a dwindling supply of party animation, I turned with a polite smile and said: "I don't think I know your niece." She gurgled with laughter. "No, I don't think so, really. I only had one niece; she promised to be quite hideously plain but died in infancy, poor thing. No, I have the dubious distinction of being *Pierre*'s aunt. When Pierre left England and came out here two years ago the family said I was the Pierre-less aunt. With the exception of Pierre, the family are revolting pun-makers. Have you met him?"

"Not boring," I thought, and said: "Pierre?"

"Pierre de Choisy. His father was French and Pierre was brought up in France, which had a very bad effect on him—too many *brioches* I expect. However, he's quite presentable now."

"I don't think I've——"

"No, well you probably haven't. The poor boy only comes in to town once in a blue moon I believe. He's in the police force, stationed at some barbarous little outpost with a most extraordinary name. Kozuti or Dokuzi or something. I do find these local names so confusing."

"You're a newcomer to Rhodesia?"

Pierre's aunt suppressed a yawn (which brought the moisture of tears to her eyes) and smiled guiltily. "Sorry! Yes, very new. Pierre kept writing wildly exciting letters about bananas and parrots and things and said I must come and see the Colonies before they disintegrated. I must say I've had a delightful time here. And I can't see any signs of disintegration at all."

"Oh, you're just on a visit?"

"Oh, yes! This is my last night. Can't imagine how anyone persuaded me to come to this ghastly party when my plane leaves at such an unearthly hour tomorrow morning. Did that woman say your name was Carol? Well, Carol my dear, I am favourably impressed. You've let me ramble on for at least ten minutes without interrupting me or attempting to foist me off on someone else. I dislike being circumspect, and anyway I haven't the time. The point is, could I send Pierre your address and would you allow the boy to take you to a cinema or something? He has his own car but, though this Doku Kuzi place may have an abundance of parrots and bananas, I doubt if there are any nice young girls for him. Would you? You *are* a dear! If you find him repulsive, just suffer one evening with him and then say you have an insane father or something and put him off. I think you will like him, though. He's full of humour and devoid of convention."

He was. He also had heavily-marked eyebrows and a keen sense of the ridiculous, and I allowed my father to retain his sanity.

Very soon after that smoke-hazed party of brittle introductions and volatile wit, I found my own moods no longer at my bidding. Like fragments of blown paper, scuttling, swirling, sinking, they were governed by the wind of Pierre's mercurial spirit, and I became his wife.

Dzokuti, the barbarous little outpost . . . the name was now pronounced with less jocularity and more respect, for it was to become my home.

\*      \*      \*

Pierre and I had driven for endless miles on rutted tracks. The tarred road from Salisbury had long since given way to an earth one, spinning itself out dustily from the wheels of the car. Cultivated land was replaced by *msasa* trees and long, seed-scattering grass. The Rhodesian summer had drifted in hazily, but the rains were late and the country still winter-dry and dun-coloured.

When the pale orange road climbed a hill and our speed decreased, we heard the shrill singing of sun-drenched insects and, flying in ungainly swoops between the trees, grey louries called "Go wa-ay!" with nasal impudence.

On completing another steep ascent in second gear we were unexpectedly confronted with a large native store with all its accoutrements of petrol pumps and Coca-Cola signs. Framed on the veranda in purple bougainvillea and scarlet geraniums stood a woman, tall and imposing, who waved distractedly. Pierre said: "That's the store-keeper's wife; she always waves." He flapped a hand at her as we passed.

Without warning we were in Dzokuti and, had we not reduced our speed, we should soon have left the few scattered houses far behind. As we passed them, Pierre indicated the tree-hidden bungalows with affection. "It's an absurd little place," he said; "only twelve of us. But live in it for a while and you find yourself treating the whole set-up seriously—almost."

The first house was the largest, surrounded by trees.

"That's the Native Commissioner's place—peculiar old coot. Blusters a lot. There's the house of the clerk of the court, Fawcett, and his wife—amusing people. Then the Land Development Officer's place—he's a new L.D.O., a South African: his wife's an emigrant—dull. The buildings opposite are the Native Department offices and court room."

We bumped over several jarring ridges and I saw a Union Jack suspended limply as Union Jacks are suspended above lonely outposts the world over, a bright symbol in fading colours. Beside the flagpole was a long building, thatched and whitewashed. "Our offices," said Pierre. "Up there behind them is the sergeant's house; Billy Burkitt and his wife, Jennifer, are pleasant people, you'll like them. The place on the hill behind them is Derek's; he's the Acting Assistant Magistrate. That's the lot, except for ourselves."

The car came to a halt in front of a very small house with windows that peered like two inquisitive eyes beneath the frill of a rusty corrugated-iron roof.

"The constable's house," finished Pierre. He regarded me with mild concern. "It was built in 1904," he said.

Our furniture had arrived in advance. That is to say, my own additions to the furniture already provided by the police force—solid chairs, cupboards with mice-droppings on the shelves, and tables with uneasy legs; the police force could not be blamed for anything but the solidity of the chairs. Mice-droppings and uneasy table-legs were a result of bachelor neglect and ill usage. I had brought a rickety towel-horse, four bookcases and five leopard skins, three of which were tail-less, due to the teething pains of an indulged puppy. Also reproductions of Laurençin and Vlaminck, the former dreamily elegant, the latter blending explosive colours with sombre shadows. With the bookcases stood a crate of kitchen utensils which would never be handled with dreary insensibility because they were bought with reckless, illogical frivolity. My irrepressible mother had danced about the shop with high heels tapping, choosing saucepans for the colour of their handles and pouncing on tempting culinary gadgets, each of which was declared to be essential.

While Pierre and I were surveying our belongings with gratification, a brown head poked round the half-open door, the eyes wide with curiosity.

"All right, come in, Langton. You can help us move these things." Pierre turned to me, "This is my cook boy. He's been with me for a year. He has often queried my celibate existence, yet ever since I told him I had taken his advice and found myself a wife he's been a bundle of nerves. He has always worked for a bachelor."

We became blissfully absorbed in the arrangement of our possessions. Langton perpetually hindered our progress, exclaiming with amazement and delight at the untold riches his master's bride had brought with her. We reached the stage, at length, when it was a matter of indifference to us both that a picture hung too high or too low, or upside down, or even that it was hung at all. The African hovered uncertainly. "What we make for dinner?" he said. The question was put to me with some deference. We made fried eggs.

Our historical little cottage was oddly designed. From the front entrance one stepped on to a small, gauzed-in veranda. There were three rooms, each one an uncompromising square of identical size. To the right our bedroom, to the left a spare room which could never be spared—it contained a turmoil of bachelor junk which no one had any intention of ever sorting out—and in the centre the living-room, which shared the requirements of dining-room and drawing-room with an invisible division between the two. The old-fashioned sash-windows were small, opened jerkily, and rattled in the wind. The floor-boards were ingrained over the years with layers of dust and floor-polish. In several places the white ant had been victorious, and we concealed the gaping holes with leopard skins—a deception soon to be deplored by visitors, when their entries and exits were punctuated by clumsy lurches which experience had taught us to avoid.

In the early days our house had served as both living-quarters and office for the single police trooper stationed in Dzokuti. Our bedroom had been the office. Strange to think of the countless, rag-clad Africans who must have shuffled in and squatted on the floor—shrill-voiced women complaining of rape; youths with spindle legs and broad, flat feet, on charges of petty theft—all in the room where I now draw my Toile de Jouy curtains in the morning, and scatter talcum powder on the floor.

The bathroom was attached to the house by a narrow extension of the roof. The kitchen and pantry claimed no relationship whatever with the house; they stood in dark and smoky petulance some twelve yards distant. In Dzokuti there was no electricity. Lamps and wood-burning stoves ruled, with all the perverse characteristics expected of them.

Our lavatory was inconvenient—a thunder-box hidden by a grass enclosure, erected so far from the house that when it rained we went there by car.

\*  \*  \*

I awoke to my first day in Dzokuti. I heard the clear fluting of the white-eyebrowed Heuglin's robin and the gay scream of Meyer's parrots that flashed blue-green past the window, constantly accompanied by a cooing turtle-dove, fat and sleek and rather simple.

Pierre sipped his tea, passive and semi-conscious. He replaced the cup blindly on the tray and slid down between the sheets as a seal slides below the ice, but he had not been long submerged when a bell rang. With flailing legs and arms, flapping khaki trousers, grey police shirt and thumping boots, he was gone. The time was a quarter past six—a time, I later discovered, when the police motor-bike, horse and Land-Rover were overhauled and groomed.

I heaved myself up to the level of the window. Our house lay on the outskirts of Dzokuti. There were no boundaries to our small property and the gravel drive wandered into oblivion a few yards from the house. The *bundu*\* crept up thus far, loitering on the verge of the tame grass, awaiting a chance to encroach yet farther. Beyond the wild and waiting grass the bundu spread with abandon across the plains and tickled the granite breast of a mountain, Wayanje. To an early morning eye the plains were aloof, drawn apart in self-contemplation and rising mist. The mist which veiled

---

\* *Bundu:* bush country, a purely Rhodesian term. The Shona word *bundu* in actual fact means a knot in wood, growth or lump. They would use the word *nyika* or *sango* when speaking in general of the country.

Wayanje sometimes lifted delicately, like the intake of a breath, to reveal her smoke-blue shoulder. At midday the blunt granite peaks would be stark against the white background of a hot sky, and the plains would shimmer, blurred and hazy below. An eagle might circle above them in high, magnificent circles, diminishing to a black particle dissolved in light.

My eyes refocused and dropped from the mist-clothed mountain to a closer scene, our garden. It was appalling. I perceived the bird-bath Pierre had described: it had remained, unmoved, since 1927 when, according to legend, it was first installed. Graceless but resolute, a dry, hollowed stone perched grimly on a high cairn of boulders; grass and weeds squabbled round its base, and lizards gleamed in its crevices. Encircling the tomb-like structure were the remains of a flower-bed: gravel and the odd self-sown zinnia, dejected and effete. The whole depressing affair was confronted by a semi-circle of brittle lawn, separated from the house-front by the gravel drive. A massive bougainvillea undulated along the ground at one end, and at the other a cascading palm staved off the advances of indigenous undergrowth. In the centre two old msasa trees stood courteously apart and linked arms when the wind blew.

Pierre returned for breakfast, after which he departed, once more in a hurry, murmuring: "Radio schedule. I'm late!" Langton cleared the table and then retired behind the banana palms for a quiet smoke before facing the strenuous business of washing the plates.

I went out to look more closely at the thirty-year-old bird-bath. Thirty years is a great age in Rhodesia. Out in the sun cicadas shrilled ceaselessly; exhaustingly tense at first, the sound imperceptibly changes until it becomes a hypnotic lullaby. Tremulous white butterflies flew erratically over the weeds. I gazed at the indestructible bird-bath and felt that something must be done.

I found the stone was not as heavy as I had imagined and carried it to the base of one of the msasa trees. Once removed from its rocky mount the bird-bath seemed less obtrusive, and looked up somewhat pathetically from the grass. I brought a bucket of water and filled the little hollow till the water slid over the edges of the rock, and glistening bubbles swung in the centre. I visualised mossy rocks and sword-fern, arum lilies, irises and agapanthus, all spreading round the base of the tree, with the brown rock pool gleaming quizzically through the leaves. The bereft cairn, however, was neither pathetic nor quizzical, its attitude was menacing and I attacked it.

The sun rose higher. My forehead was damp, and a pea-sized blister puffed up protestingly on the palm of my hand; but stone by stone the cairn was being demolished. Lizards flickered out and spiders rose on thin legs and stalked away with dignity.

Tottering wearily to the grass verge, embracing yet another dusty rock, I heard an approaching car and turned to see an opulent black Buick sweep up to the house. The promptness of my first caller was unexpected. She remained at the wheel of the car till I approached, then smiled at me in a way which I was to learn was inimitably hers—dropping her head on one side, half-closing her eyes, and smiling with lips compressed, all in one quick movement, the desired and attained effect being both gracious and intimate. At her shoulder an impudent Pekingese rested its chin on its paws and sniffed. My visitor introduced herself: "Hallo! I'm Betty Harker. There's no need to say who *you* are, my dear, as I know you must be Pierre's wife, Carol. I've heard *so* much about you! I really shan't stay for more than a minute; I can see you were busy. I just came down to see if there was anything you might need. Porky, get down at once! Ah, you're tackling the bird-bath! I simply adore gardening; it brings one so close to nature, but I never garden now because it simply ruins my hands. Porky *darling*, weedgy, woodgy, weedgy!" She stepped out with Porky under her arm and I recognised the imposing woman who had waved at us from the store on the previous day. She swayed on her high heels, a veritable Athena. A dress of mustard-yellow draped her well-developed figure, and her auburn hair was swept up with combs to form an impressive pyramid of waves and rolls that seemed in no danger of collapsing. The Pekingese struggled for freedom, but was pressed with increasing fervour to her bosom, where it eventually subsided. Mrs Harker's head dropped to one side again as she smiled. "Isn't he sweet? My little Porky-pie, what *would* Mumsy do without you?" Reflecting that one must never show dismay at inopportune calls, I led a willing Mrs Harker on to the veranda. A glance through the living-room door confirmed my apprehensions: the room was still in a state of utter confusion. However, my guest's unconcealed curiosity compelled me to invite her inside for tea.

"Books!" she cried, stepping delicately between them to reach a chair. "How simply lovely! I adore reading, though of course I never have the time. Basil adores books, too—my husband, you know. He's a brilliant man, really; I always say he should have gone into politics. He does so miss things here, people with whom he can talk on the same level I mean." She released Porky at this point and he trotted purposefully out of the door in the direction of the kitchen.

"My dear, you've done *wonders*—absolutely charming! Of course, you know Pierre had it all painted before you came. I chose the paint for him, I knew you'd like it. I offered to help paint the walls myself, I do love to see a job well done, but dear Pierre wouldn't hear of it. I believe he called a prisoner in to help him." She cocked her head on one side and smiled warmly, "I almost feel as though he was my own son—Pierre, I mean." She smoothed her hair with tapering, crimson nails. "You'd never think I was fifty, would you? In such a small community as ours one comes to know people inside out. Pierre is old enough to be my son-in-law, at all events. Of course, you know I have four daughters? Isn't it wonderful? Elinore, Myrtle, Rosemary, and Maureen, all at boarding school except my eldest, Elinore. She's at a finishing school in Switzerland. *Lovely* child. . . ."

I was forced to break into her monologue by calling to Langton to make tea. I offered Mrs Harker a cigarette and lit one myself. She appeared to possess qualities of infinite resource and inexhaustible energy. Her voice was full-throated and loud and she exercised a forceful and dominant personality. I asked: "How long have you been at Dzokuti?"

"Oh, years and years! We've watched them come and go —police, Native Commissioners, L.D.O.s. And the stories I could tell about them! The last N.C.'s wife, Eva Jones—but I never repeat scandal. Ah, here comes the tea, how quick! And dear little Porky! Where *have* you been, my little precious?"

Langton felt his way into the room with the tea-tray, adroitly avoiding the rodent-like teeth of Porky.

"Porky, you naughty little boy, come here at once! He's perfectly harmless really, he just wants to protect his mistress, bless his little heart!"

"Milk, Mrs Harker?"

"Oh, black, dear. I'm on a rigorous diet. *No* more than nine hundred calories a day, that's my allowance. Of course, I generally allow myself a little more, about eleven hundred. But do call me Betty; no one stands on ceremony in Dzokuti. That is, no one but the present N.C.'s wife, Daphne Fanshawe. It's been Mrs Harker and Mrs Fanshawe ever since she came. Of course, I don't deny she has a position to main-

tain, but I do think it a pity, when after all there are only
five of us women—six now you're here. But you couldn't
meet a nicer person than Daphne and I don't hold her
formality against her one little bit."

During the course of Betty's chatter I altered my expression
to suit the tone she employed; nothing more was required of
me, as a reply of more than three words would have constituted
an interruption. We sipped our tea in silence for a moment
and I contemplated the likelihood of drawing her into
expressing her views on the other inhabitants of Dzokuti. If
she were prepared to give opinions on them all with the
candour she had shown in discussing the Native Commissioner's wife, I felt it would be senseless not to avail myself of
the opportunity of hearing them. But I was thwarted. She
put her cup down firmly on the arm of the chair, glanced
brightly round the room, and said: "Of course, I think all
Gainsborough's pictures are absolutely marvellous. One of
my closest friends, Lady Tolemly, has a superb original of
his, a full-length portrait, in her hall. Of course, I have a
considerable number of rather good old family heirlooms
myself—silver and odd things, Chippendale, Sheraton,
rather good old pieces of furniture, you know. But, of course,
it would never do to bring them out here, what with the
climate and the servants and all."

We talked at some length on the climate, the ineptitude of
African servants, and the rising prices of commodities—the
conventional subjects which give so many housewives such
intense pleasure to discuss. Langton reappeared on silent feet
to remove the tray, and Mrs Harker rose on her stiletto
heels, gathering Porky into her arms. "My dear, I *have* en-
joyed our cosy little chat. I may call you Carol? You simply
*must* come up to the store any time you wish, I'd love to see
you. Bring Pierre one evening and have a drink with us."
The parting smile over her shoulder was offset by her Pekingese

who peered at me from beneath her chin with an expression of insolent smugness. I followed her to the car and watched her arrange herself at the wheel. Porky took up his stance at the window and, with her long, dipped nose and determined chin thrust forward, Betty pressed the accelerator and the car shot down the drive.

When he returned to the house for lunch Pierre said that Betty Harker was quite a nice old bag, really. "One could use that inane expression 'she means well'," he said, "but the thing is that with Betty one isn't sure whether she always means well or not."

The afternoon was brief and at half-past four, unless some unusual circumstance delayed them, the Civil Servants of Dzokuti were covering typewriters and closing files.

"Derek Vaughn has asked us to go over this evening for a drink," said Pierre. "Before we go, I'd like to take you on a tour of inspection round the police camp."

Behind our house the ground rose steeply, covered with tangled grass, clumps of banana palms and drooping mango trees. A grass fence ran up one side, forming a shaky barrier between us and the prisons—three small buildings with heavily bolted doors and high, barred windows. As a rule in country districts prisons come under the administration of the police, who are in turn responsible to the Federal Prison Service. Close to the prisons were a store-room and a stable, which exuded the familiarly strong and pleasant odour of cut grass, ammonia and horse-sweat. The occupant, Dick Turpin, was grazing in a paddock. He was old and rather stout.

Beyond were the cottages of the African constables, neatly white-washed and surrounded by hard-baked earth, well swept and devoid of vegetation. Piccanins rolled the rusty wheel of a bicycle about the parade ground and stared at us with popping eyes, showing both disappointment and relief when we turned away toward the office.

The building was thatch-roofed with no ceiling, and the cool air rose to the rafters, where wasps' nests of mud clung like pouched cheeks to the cross-beams. Pierre pivoted on his heels and surveyed the room with his hands behind his back.

"To your right you see a map of the Dzokuti district farms and native reserve," he said. "The map is reasonably accurate. To your left you see a calendar suspended below a picture of a peachy blonde whose significance in connection with the B.S.A. police is uncertain, though I suppose one could label her as Type Most Likely to Feature in a Sex Murder. Hanging beside her is our selection of handcuffs, all sizes. Some of them may even be collector's pieces in 1970 when handcuffs will probably be obsolete. The box files above your head are neatly assigned to such diverse subjects as Native Eating Houses and High Court Decisions."

Pierre also demonstrated the Dolphin radio, which seemed perplexingly involved. The range of transmission and reception was impressive. In remote districts the police radio often supplies the only means of immediate contact with the outside world. Regularly at eight o'clock in the morning and three o'clock in the afternoon all stations were linked, I was told, by a general police broadcast and communicated with each other. Their messages, to which I later listened, seemed to consist largely of the words, able, Charlie, dog, fox and ink.

"Here on the desk," said Pierre, "is Crime and Punishment, with apologies to Dostoyevsky. It's the crime register where all the foul deeds of men are recorded. Before I become too waggish about everything, we'd better beetle along to Derek's place."

A narrow path with a constant traffic of grasshoppers

separated us from the dwelling of Derek Vaughn. His house was as new as ours was old—utilitarian but comfortable, with a low roof and pink-washed walls. The surrounding property was rambling and neglected. Immediately in front of the house, however, was an orderly patch where marigolds and zinnias provided a gaudy mass of colour. Half-hidden among the yellows and scarlets I glimpsed the shoulders and fair head of a man. He was crouched on the ground with a fork in one hand, vigorously loosening the surface of the earth and pausing at intervals to wipe his forehead, by which action he unknowingly bestowed broad streaks of brown above his pale eyebrows. A tortoiseshell cat circled about him, stiff-legged with tail erect, purring softly to gain his attention. Patiently marking the imprudent advances of a lizard, a tabby cat sat at the edge of the flower bed with tensely humped back and twitching tail tip. A black cat was stretched with boneless grace on the veranda step. Derek Vaughn glanced up as we approached, but made no attempt to alter his position.

"How do you do?" he drawled, without waiting for Pierre's introduction. "How do you like Dzokuti? Personally I am appalled at the number of bugs it harbours." He continued to wield the fork and, as there seemed no alternative, Pierre and I sat on the grass beside him and exchanged desultory platitudes. As his eyes were intent on his cultivation I studied his face. It was long and effeminate with a thin, sharp nose, a girlish mouth and cool grey eyes. He had the type of complexion which never defeats the sun, and the back of his neck was very red. His whole expression was one of supercilious amiability.

At last he flung down his fork, rubbed the purring tortoiseshell beneath its chin and unbent his long legs.

"Come and have a drink. I fail to remember just what there is in the liquor line but I have a hazy recollection of seeing a half-empty gin bottle—or would it sound more promising if I said a half-full one?"

Some men lope rather than walk, and it was with a definite lope that Derek preceded us into his house. The drawing-room was a little startling. Red and black were the predominant colours. Red and black cubes danced with surrealistic enthusiasm across the curtains. The black-spotted upholstery seemed to quiver with life, and cushions glowed flaming red in the armchairs. Above the fireplace was a curious contrivance: nails had been driven into the wall with intentional haphazardness, and twisting snakily from nail to nail were yards of black insulating wire. The striking effect of black on white and the animated appearance of the wire had a weird appeal, but after the first few minutes of scrutiny the whole contraption seemed rather to betray an immature mind.

On the mantelpiece below stood a copper bowl in which granadilla leaves and marigolds were arranged with delicacy and skill. Reproductions of Braque and Picasso decorated the remaining walls. With its broken forms and hectic lines Picasso's "Lady in a Rocking Chair" was particularly well suited to the room. The floor in the picture appeared to be rocking with the lady, and the lady herself had become so completely entangled with her chair that escape was out of the question. Her one recognisable eye expressed her horror of the situation.

"Have you written any poetry lately, Keats?" asked Pierre. Derek gave an exaggerated wince at the appellation. He handed me a gin and lime, presented an open box of cigarettes, signalled to Pierre to help himself, and sank languidly into an arm-chair.

"As a matter of fact, I have, since you mention it, Pierre. Some of it was too unbelievably mundane, and some moderately successful and accepted for publication in *Transi-*

*tive Fundamentals*. But none of it satisfies me at all. Not at all."
He dropped his head back and looked reflectively at the
ceiling, swinging his foot. "I don't really know that this is the
place . . . nothing to induce one to any creative efforts . . .
atmosphere of intellectual wreckage . . . miles of bundu."

"Surely," I said, "what could be more helpful? Complete
seclusion and no social distractions. Your evenings and weekends are not infringed upon, and all the tranquillity of
Parnassus lies at your doorstep."

Derek interlaced his fingertips with precision and said:
"My dear Mrs de Choisy, the tranquillity is irrefutable—on
the surface. But you are a newcomer to the Dzokuti scene
and not yet quite aware of the little cross-currents of calumny
and intrigue. I am *frequently* molested over weekends and I
assure you I have been driven to the most desperate measures.
You see, were I living in town, it would be only too simple
to be *out*, but in Dzokuti one really *has* to be out, or else one
is so obviously *in*, if you see what I mean. No subterfuge is
possible."

"To what desperate measures have you been driven?" I
asked.

"We-ell, a majestic black Buick descends on me from time
to time and I have formed the most unsociable habit of
barring my front door over weekends; in fact, I set up a
minor barricade and when I hear tyres on the gravel I rush
trembling to my bedroom and peer distractedly through a
slit in the curtains. Admittedly she usually takes the locked
door as a sign of no entry, and after a few tentative coo-ees
and taps on the window panes, she withdraws defeated.
Pierre himself has joined me once or twice in my ignominious
run for cover."

Pierre said: "Only because your odd behaviour forced me
to! I mean, what on earth could I say if she found me lurking
about here alone?"

"Say you were collecting cigarette stubs," said Derek.

We talked for a time about snakes, the heat and racial problems. "Could I borrow your copy of Paton's *Cry the Beloved Country*, or the other thing he wrote, *No More the Philanthropist* or something," said Pierre suddenly. "Everyone seems to have read one or the other."

Derek finished his drink with a gulp and rose to refill his glass. "Never waste your time with books that everyone seems to have read," he said. "If everyone has read them, you will soon become thoroughly familiar with the book without so much as lifting the cover. You will have it brilliantly analysed and concisely summarised by all your acquaintances; you will hear condensed and simplified versions while you wait to be served in a bottle store; and you will listen to protracted, amplified and interminable versions while you wait to be served in a chemist's shop. I will now give you a concise summary of it myself. It makes me positively *curl*. It panders to the sentimentality of the common herd. If people feel sorry for the unfortunate lot of the black boy—and well they may in South Africa—then I do wish they would do something practical about it without having to *drool*. A great many of our friends in England are not unnaturally becoming bored with our repeated chant 'The African *has* a long way to go', but it's so absolutely true. You can't hoist a child from his nursery tea and expect him to preside at a Rotary Club dinner."

Having dismissed the *Beloved Country*, Derek introduced the subject of Yoga. He had been reading a book on the subject and he gave us a condensed and simplified account of the book. He also amplified his comments with aphorisms which he told us he had garnered from the translations of the ancient writings of an Indian called Patanjali. "The essential thing is *Pratyahara*," he said airily.

"What's that?"

"The elimination of distracting influences. All fearfully interesting, I dabbled in it. But the trouble is the servants— it's so awfully embarrassing explaining one's postures to them, and, if one doesn't explain at all, their inevitable conclusion is that one is insane, and their subsequent attitude towards one is *nerve*-racking!"

Sultry heat and the fourth gin and lime had somewhat blurred my perceptions so that when we came to discuss Derek's pictures I felt that Pierre and Derek delivered their judgements with a rare and subtle discernment.

"I regard modern art as a challenge," said Derek.

"A challenge to what?" said Pierre.

"Well, a *challenge*. I mean, what you see is what the artist *felt*. It's the reaction of the subject on his subconscious mind. That still life over there, it has an unearthly beauty!"

"Yes, possibly. But what is it?"

"What is it? Why should that matter? It can be whatever you like. It can be something different every day. But whatever it is, the artist has caught the *essence* of it. The conception and the execution come from a mind that was strung taut, and—and quivered with what it saw."

"Oh! Well, I suppose that explains the indistinctness. But it's really sort of quasi-primitive."

"That wonderful splash of orange *is* primitive, admirably so. Only a mind uncluttered by the commonplace conventions could have conceived such a master-stroke. But you'd prefer a pretty scene? You can't realise that artists are capable of outgrowing mere copyism and using their art as a means of self-expression?"

"Seems grossly unfair that they should reveal their most objectionable moods and expect a gratified public to pay exorbitantly for the revelation."

"You'd like the face to be cut-and-dried, with the eye-lashes plainly visible?" said Derek bitingly. "The trouble with you, my dear Pierre, is that you have a child-like desire to understand the painting at a glance and tell yourself with smug sureness: 'Oh yes, that's a so-and-so,' before you settle back placidly to admire the colours."

"Oh, I *see*," said Pierre. "With these, one must appreciate the crudity of the colours at a glance, murmuring: 'That wonderful orange' . . . before settling back placidly to detect the subject, or, rather, the artist's interpretation of the essence of the subject."

Derek refused to be irritated. "You'll see them as I do one day," he prophesied. "You'll learn to love the vitality of cubism and the exaltant colours of Fauvism, and the disturbing spiritualism of expressionism."

Pierre said: "And the 'swiftism' of the descent to plagiarism?"

"Unkind!" said Derek with a broad smile.

(The unceasing, unsettled conflict between upholders of different schools of painting—between the realistic reproduction and the imaginative conception—is a curious thing. Both parties remain entirely unconvinced by the other's views, but each is frantically anxious to convert the other to its own. The subject draws as much heat as it did more than thirty years ago, and the artists of that period are still involved. When Derek spoke of modern art he was refering to Braque, or Matisse, or Villon, and not, as might be expected, to John Piper or Graham Sutherland, who were born in the present century.

There are some painters, also belonging to the "moderns", who seldom become involved in this perennial strife: the bright delicacy of a Legueult, the haunting airiness of a Laprade, and the trembling, nervous sparkle of a Monticelli are overshadowed by the toppling vases and ponderous, dull-eyed nudes of other more-talked-of painters, though they, too, have a certain fascination.)

Before we left, Derek insisted upon my accepting a gift
of soap. He had made a quantity of soap that day.

"Such a satisfying substance to handle!" he drawled. "I
use butter and various other things—citronella—don't take
that untinted stuff, it looks like a rather inferior Cheddar.
Here's a good lump of the pink—drop of cochineal did the
trick."

\*          \*          \*

The time was somewhere within the hour before midnight
when Pierre and I awoke simultaneously. Perhaps the rising
wind had been the cause. Whatever it was, once awake, we
experienced no immediate desire for sleep. Pierre sang in the
dark, throatily:

> *Venez donc chez moi' Madame,*
> *Je vous invite,*
> *Venez donc chez moi, Madame. . . .*

The telephone rang in sudden and shrill opposition, as
though unable to contain its disapproval. "Where are the
bloody matches?" said Pierre, fumbling in the dark. He lit
a candle and flung on my dressing-gown with a dramatic
flourish. As he hastened to the door the candle threw up a
giant silhouette—a masculine profile above a trailing, frilly-
sleeved gown; it looked like some grotesque caricature of
Florence Nightingale. But a crease between the eyebrows and
a firm mouth denoted a rejection of levity, a consciousness of
responsibilities, obligations, duty. Immoderate feminine
laughter would be a mistake. I heard him speak in the adjoin-
ing room and raised my head.

"Police camp here, yes? Oh, is that you, Mr Harvey . . .
yes, yes, I see. Right. We'll be along right away. No, of
course not. That's quite all right . . . yes." The telephone was
replaced with a clatter and Pierre came back to the bedroom

B

and said: "Murder, my sweet!" I sat up with pleasantly chilling thoughts of Agatha Christie situations. "Who? Where?"

"Oh, a place called Chipinje farm, about twenty miles from here. According to Harvey an African woman has been killed in his compound. I'll have to wake Billy and collect some A.C.s.* Have your beauty sleep, I'll be away some time." While he spoke he divested himself of the incongruous pink frills and struggled into his uniform, and a minute later he had blown me a kiss and hurried from the room.

I lay listening and presently heard the rumble of the Land-Rover's engine above the whooping wind. I strained to catch the faint increase of sound as it climbed the hills beyond Dzokuti.

The candle was left burning. The shadows it cast on the walls quivered convulsively and the curtains were swept out and sucked in with the bellying swell of a sail at sea. Then the wind dropped and I became conscious of persistent, indefinable sounds, more felt than heard. Small creeping noises that sometimes exploded with a definite *tick*...when the house would produce a silence as horrified as my own, for a moment, before the elusive, stifled sounds were audible again. I deliberately sustained my pleasant apprehensions by thinking of the strange assortment of people the house must have harboured since 1904—lonely policemen whose minds had swayed over the boundary of balance because of their solitude; wholesome young troopers with pink cheeks becoming sallow and soured through lack of wholesome company; and the statements and hysterical accusations made in this same room by terrified Africans, victims of brutal violence or insidious witchcraft. Possibilities, each increasingly harrowing and unlikely, flitted into my range of thought and were accepted with credulity. But the thoughts that oppressed my mind

* A.C.: African constable.

eventually caused its insensibility by their repetitive insistence. The candle guttered and burnt out while I slept.

When I awoke again the room was still dark but the wind had died. I heard a muted gurgle that at first suggested a horribly prolonged strangulation but turned into a good imitation of escaping bath-water. Then, with the delicate fragrance of Johnson's baby talcum-powder floating about him, Pierre entered on tip-toe wrapped in a towel.

"You're awake? I've just had a bath. Necessity after shuffling about in that reeking hut! The poor woman's relatives and cronies were absolutely packed round her, redolent of *bouquet d'Afrique*."

"Yes, but tell me about the murder!"

"Well, if I can't sleep till you've heard all the details, I'll give you the repellent story in a nutshell. We got our man, as they say. I should think he'll probably get about seven years for culpable homicide. When we got to Harvey's compound his boss boy met us and told us the woman was dead. You could hear them all wailing in her hut. We had to call the mob out before we could get in. Found her lying on the floor with a lake of blood under her head. She wasn't dead, but she was unconscious. We were told that her assailant, who happened to be her husband, had gone to the compound on Bullen's farm, so we had to leave her to the mercies of her mourners. Took us quite a time to reach Bullen's place, because there isn't a short cut and we had to get back on to the main road. When we arrived at the compound there, we found those wretched Apostles were holding a meeting under the stars. They were sitting in a circle, singing hymns, and the man we were after was with them, squatting on his heels with his hands over his face and rocking from side to side. The whole story was typically garbled. Apparently he'd been drunk and had hit his wife on the head with the back of an axe. His reason for hitting her was that he had discovered she had given some of his beer to another woman. She had given the beer to the other woman because the other woman had helped her to thatch their hut. Draw a deep breath—ye gods! And some misguided fools say they are capable of self-government!

"Anyway, he admitted the whole thing, so we collected him and the witnesses and went back for the woman. Then we had to take her to the native clinic. The orderly there cut the hair away from her wound with a razor and it looked damn awful. She'd had a frightful bash and her skull had actually caved in a bit. The orderly said he thought she would live, they're so tough, but she died while he was speaking."

I dreamed of candle shadows that swayed over the walls and were transformed into huge shapes which my dream logic told me were Apostles; and Derek Vaughn sat in the centre of them, in a bird-bath. His hands were over his face, but he kept spreading his fingers apart and peeping through them.

## CHAPTER TWO

"IS anyone at home?" A voice chirped at the front door. The caller was petite and pretty, with a freckled, retroussé nose, and on her head a scarf that did not quite conceal the silver tips of curling pins.

"I'm Jennifer Burkitt. Hope I'm not being a nuisance; I just felt like having a gossip."

Jennifer was soon contentedly settled in one of the faded deck-chairs on the veranda. "Marvellous idea of Pierre's to get married!" she said. "You've no idea how bloody well browned off I get sometimes. You see all the other wives in Dzokuti have their husbands coming home from the office as regular as clockwork mostly, and there I sit, waiting for Billy, who's probably rushing about like a demon on the motor-bike doing a patrol, or out on some case or other. Now you've come, we can barge across the parade ground to each

35

other and hold hands, so to speak, because you'll be in the same boat yourself."

I agreed. A picture of Pierre rushing about on the motorbike like a demon flashed upon the inward eye and depressed me.

"It's beastly," said Jennifer. "I don't think I'll ever get used to it. I've had five years of it. But Billy loves his job and so long as he's happy. . . ."

Like Derek, Jennifer asked me what I thought of Dzokuti, and like Derek she did not expect a reply and gave me no time to make one. "There's an awful lot of gossip," she went on. "Always is in a little station like this. Nothing exciting. I mean no adulteries, suicides or embezzlements. Just nice, cosy gossip. You won't be able to join in till you know us all better so I'll do the gossiping today. You've met Betty Harker already. I saw her tearing down to you in a cloud of dust yesterday. She's an absolute scream. Billy says she's a 'climber', like a morning glory. He also says she wants to be a nymph without the mania. But she has a heart of gold. The Native Commissioner's wife is a poppet. She's always charming and reserved, probably because she *is* the N.C.'s wife. But she's exactly the same, whether she's speaking to her servants or to any of us. Never gets ruffled and never gossips. I think she was a governess or mother's help or something like that before she married Fanshawe.

"Then there's Brenda Fawcett. Brenda's quite amusing. She and Michael used to live in the Bahamas. They still do, in a way. They're always talking about the Bahamas. The rum punch and the wild Bahama parties. Brenda's always at her happiest when she's telling you about all the young men who ran after her in the Bahamas. Must have been slimmer then. We also have the L.D.O.'s wife, Irma Dutoit. Bit insipid. Hates Rhodesia. Can't bear her native servants. Someone once said she used to go dancing with a West

African negro when she was a typist in Liverpool, but if she did he must have ditched her—it's the most interesting thing one ever hears about her. That's the lot. Quite a nice bunch, by and large. Better with their husbands. Inclined to be catty on their own, we all are. Well, I must be toddling off." She stood up. "Tell me if I'm a bore, but I do like having a natter in the mornings and it's nice having someone new to gossip with. Gets awful dull going over the same old ground with the women here. Discussing Betty with Brenda and then going and discussing Brenda with Betty." She lingered, kicking the veranda step and loth to go. Smiling whimsically, she recalled further anecdotes illustrating the reserve of Mrs Fanshawe, the coquetry of Mrs Harker, the affectation of Mrs Fawcett and the vacuity of Mrs Dutoit. When some ten minutes had elapsed, I wondered whether we should not resume our chairs, but she descended another step as she said: "Did Betty tell you, by the way, of the Great Event?"

"No."

"Glory be! I thought she'd talk of nothing else. We're planning a dance in February—all of us Dzokuti types and the local farmers. Decided it was time we had a big get-together. It's going to be held in the Ellis-Parkers' tobacco barn, or grading shed or something. Of course, Betty Harker will automatically become organiser-in-chief and we lesser females fall back submissively and bow to her superior powers. The woman's born to it. She overrides all our tentative suggestions, and most of us can't be bothered to assert ourselves, anyway. You'll be roped in to shoving millions of cocktail sausages on to toothpicks or something when the time comes. Well, I really must be toddling."

Half-way down the drive Jennifer turned and called:

"Glory be! I had a good excuse for calling on you and I forgot to use it! Billy told me to tell you that if you want to

ride old Dick Turpin you have his full permission. The old
bastard needs more exercise than he gets."

\*          \*          \*

Dick Turpin bore me at an amble along a dusty track that
had caught my eye from the main road. The main road, with
the attraction of its native stores, had been littered with
African pedestrians and cyclists; picturesque though they
were, their curiosity when they saw me, and animated discussions as to who I might be and where I might be going,
and why, had inclined me to seek a less populated path. The
old horse was at first plainly puzzled by my desire for solitude.
When the drab grey of weathered thatch had appeared
between the trees, his soft brown eyes had been alive with
interest, and he had stepped out purposefully towards the
kraal. 'This is a familiar trend of events,' he must have
thought, 'the first patrol target.' When I turned him away,
he stumbled sullenly in the long grass and stretched his neck
to grab the odd mouthful. 'We might as well resign ourselves to a botany ramble.'

By mid-morning, that is to say a hot morning in early
November, the bush is hushed into a sort of drowsy stillness.
Before the summer's first fall of rain the dryness hums like a
singing in one's eardrums. There is little other singing; it is
the rain that puts the songs into the throats of birds, and an
inclination to grow into the veins of the grass. We drew up
once and, without the soft thud of Dick Turpin's big hooves
and swish of his tail, the silence became oppressive. When we
moved again, he trod on a dry branch and the explosive
snapping of it seemed almost to call for an apology to the
hostile, listening trees. As though the crack had been a
signal, a cicada near by burst into a harsh "tzzzeee".

A filigree pattern ran beside us in the dust—an African's
broad feet weaving through the deeper impressions left by

his cattle; the light prints of a dog's paws, some rib-hollow cur that had trotted loyally beside its master; and threading delicately in and out were the dainty split triangles left by a duiker's hooves.

After a time Dick Turpin's ears lost their eager prick; he became insensible to all but the rhythmic movement of his legs, and his eyelids drooped. When roused, he broke into an indignant trot, alert to further provocation. None came. He lifted his head, snorted, and swung into a lurching, rocking-horse canter.

A mongoose sprang into the path some yards ahead, seeing us with one eye as it landed. It stopped for a stupefied second with lifted paw, nose twitching, then scampered away with its head low—repugnant horror personified from its hunched shoulders to the tip of its rigid tail.

We came upon a sweep of land that had suffered the vicious scorching of a bush fire. Indomitable acacias and msasa trees, rustled their burnt brown leaves, yet lived, but the grass was a black graveyard for countless charred beetles, which lay forlornly on their backs, their brief lives further shortened by destiny. Old stumps still smouldered and thin wisps of smoke curled into the sky. It was a place of mourning, and a bird lamented, a low, plaintive, "troo, troo, troo, *wheeeuw*". With the first heavy rains, though, the black grass tussocks would hold bright spears of green, and wild flowers would be early unfurling over the ash and cinders. Mushrooms had already appeared in their sudden, mysterious manner; scattered in white puffs about the earth, they had split in the relentless sun—over-baked meringues, shrunken and discoloured.

The bush crept about us with increasing density. Creepers writhed from tree to tree like insatiable lovers, tired of one embrace yet eager for another, and acacia thorns inscribed sharp white crosses through the sunburn on my arms. I heard the blurred song of flies and the metallic *tonk* of a cow-bell. Somewhere native cattle browsed, long-horned, mottle-skinned and fly-harassed, but they were hidden from me. They and their herd boys who set bird-snares and played *tsoro** with pebbles in the sand.

Dick Turpin was bored again : shoving his hooves slip-slop into the dust, refusing to lift them. His soft, black nostrils vibrated with heartrending sighs, until I felt quite apologetic and awkward. I tried to beguile him with a song, first in a reedy soprano, then in a ruptured contralto. He plodded on, scuffing the dust, not in the least diverted. The trees thinned at last, and beyond them the glaring white sand of a dry river bed gave some stimulus to our meanderings, and curiosity quickened his pace.

Dead reeds rattled at what had been the water's edge. Driftwood lying heavy in the forks of every tree along the bank were the only sign to tell of a flood-water's turbulent surging— thunderous brown waters that had raced for the sea and left this hot sand panting far behind. Slime-rimmed, stagnant pools had also stayed behind: some of the water had lost the race.

Dick Turpin stamped at malignant sand-flies that clung persistently to his rippling withers. The dry river bed was no longer interesting. He shook his head and flecks of green saliva sprayed from the bit. 'Let's get on with this blasted botany ramble.'

We trudged round a hill and surprised a family of rock-rabbits sunning themselves on the high granite boulders. They fled over the crest of the hill, bouncing up the sheer rock sides on tiny, rubbery pads. One small dassie found himself left all alone on a narrow ledge, facing our approach; he shrunk into his plump cinnamon body and desperately hoped that he looked like a stone of no significance. I waved a hand in cheery recognition and he sat up, appalled. There

* *Tsoro :* Shona word for game somewhat resembling draughts.

was only one way of retreat left to him—the narrow, per-
pendicular fissure that soared above his quivering back. He
braced himself with a foot against either side of the crevice
and, with remarkable muscular agility for so pudgy a
creature, levered himself rapidly up between the granite
walls, his fat bottom rocking from side to side. When he
reached the top he paused a moment on the skyline, a furry
globule, wiped a whisker and reflected on the nimbleness of
his escape. He wiped another whisker and reflected on the
horrors he'd seen. Then he vanished.

When Dick Turpin discovered that we were no longer outward bound, his humour improved and we crashed between
the trees at a flying trot. In this exhilarating manner we returned to the path we had followed earlier, and found ourselves bringing up the rear of a sadly bleating flock of goats.
The two piccanins who herded them stopped open-mouthed
to watch us; the goats dispersed into the bush and balanced
on their hind legs to reach the pale new leaf buds. Left by
himself in the middle of the path was the smallest, thinnest,
flea-bitten puppy that ever stumbled hopefully towards my
heart. He had a cavity where there should have been a foot-
ball tummy, and his urchin face was wrinkled with anxiety.
Dick Turpin sidled and pulled on his bit while the piccanins
clung to each other in dismay, only prevented from bolting
by a fear that the monstrous horse would overtake them.

"*Mena funa tenga lo kambganana*,"* I said with a tranquil-
lising voice and a bland smile. The piccanins were quick to
hide their astonishment; they dropped their eyes and discussed the matter between themselves in husky undertones;
they shot sly glances at the puppy. Ants ran over Dick Turpin's unconscious hooves and the puppy sank patiently on to
his haunches and dangled his tongue at me. At length some
agreement was reached, but the piccanins were both un-

* Kitchen Kaffir (lingua-franca) : I wish to buy the puppy.

willing to shoulder the responsibility of spokesman. One
nudged the other and received a nudge in return. Several
more nudges were exchanged. It all became a little trying
and I assumed another smile, blander than ever. A final
nudge, and the spokesman was elected. He snatched the
puppy by its hind leg and held it yelping aloft.

"Fivee sillings!"

Quite unreasonable. I looked away in silence.

"Four an' sickis!"

Absurd.

"Tree sillings!"

Absolute nonsense. But just when his owner suggested
"Two an' sickis?" in a chastened tone, the puppy squealed
with fear and frustration and thus became mine—for two
an' sickis. With many explanations, and some curious mis-
understandings, I finally managed to convey my wish that
the puppy be brought to Dzokuti police camp.

As I slid the saddle from Dick Turpin's wet back, Pierre
came into the stable and said: "Come up to the store with
me. I'm going to collect the meat ration for the bandits and,
if you keep a sharp lookout, you might see Betty Harker's
husband."

Upon first entering the store I had difficulty in seeing at all,
so sudden was the change from the outside glare to the dim
darkness of the store's interior. I stooped beneath an array
of cheap, ready-made dresses that swung from a wire across
the room, and straightened to see a chattering throng of
Africans who came to buy and stayed all day to gossip. The
capable Betty Harker stood behind the counter. A flutter of
brown hands reached toward her, accompanied by vociferous
demands, and she dealt out matches and sticky buns with a
certain majestic grace. Her moulded grey silk dress appeared
a little incongruous, offset as it was by bolts of brightly

coloured cottons, bars of mottled soap, torch batteries, tins of condensed milk and jam, pots, pans, paraffin, bottles of lemonade, strings of glass beads, bicycle pumps, and mousetraps.

She surged forward when she caught sight of us.

"How very nice to see you!"

"We've come for the prisoners' meat ration," said Pierre.

"Of course! Basil, prisoners' meat for Pierre." Only then did I observe another figure behind the counter. He was a plump, stocky man; his sandy hair had receded considerably, and the top of his head was satin-smooth and covered with red-brown freckles that toned well with his horn-rimmed spectacles—a fleeting impression of a lesser spotted tawny owl.

He came forward into the semi-light, blinking, and Betty introduced us. "How do you like Dzo-k-k-kuti?" he asked me, but Betty cut him short. "We can't keep Pierre and Carol waiting all day, Basil. Do go and see to the meat." Her husband retreated unobtrusively, and she turned back to us with her intimate smile.

"Isn't the weather dreadful? I can hardly believe my little Elinore is muffled up with woollies in Switzerland! I had a letter from her just the other day. She mentions you, Pierre! At least, she doesn't actually mention you by name, but she said something about charming Frenchmen and I *know* she was thinking of you!" She winked at Pierre and smiled at me to show that it was all just light-hearted banter. Basil Harker reappeared at her elbow with the parcel of meat, soggily wrapped in brown paper.

"Really, Basil, what ages you take! I'm sure Pierre and Carol must be impatient to go. It's nearly closing time. Enoch! Tell all these people to go, and come and sweep this floor, it's filthy!" She dispersed a buzzing cloud of flies with her hand. Basil looked at us and said diffidently: "C-c-can't

you c-c——", but Betty intervened with brusque kindness:
"Come and have a drink? Of course you must, you're not in
a hurry to go, are you?" We were enveloped in dust from
Enoch's broom and side-stepped to avoid the crumpled
newspapers and empty tins that were swept before him.
"We'd love to," I said.

We were ushered through a side door into the Harkers'
drawing-room. Photographs of Betty's four daughters, from
infancy to adolescence, adorned the walls, the mantelpiece,
and the top of a bookcase. I examined them and murmured
uncertain comments on each one before allowing myself to
be seated. There was a light tap of scurrying feet overhead
and Betty grimaced. "Rats! Horrid things!"

Presumably addressing me, though he looked at the carpet,
Basil said: "Perhaps *you'll* be hearing the patter of little feet
one of these days!" He coughed and relapsed into silence.

"I'm dying to see your trousseau," said Betty. "I'm sure
you've got heaps of lovely things. Of course, you know,
nylons weren't on the market when I was a bride. I bought
the loveliest nightie in Salisbury the other day, didn't I,
Basil? Gossamer sheer. I suppose your nighties are all quite
transparent?" Startled by this familiarity, I said: "Yes, all
of them." But Mrs Harker plunged on without listening:
"Veronica Barnett has the most exquisite underwear, hasn't
she, Basil? Oh, but how silly of me, how could *you* know? She
showed me all her frillies once. Have you met the Barnetts
yet, Carol, Grahame and Veronica? A delightful young
couple. Of course you know they're very well connected. . . ."
We were given a confusing account of the Barnetts' connec-
tions and all the ramifications.

"Oh, my dear!" said Mrs Harker suddenly. "I can't think
how I forgot to tell you about it! We're planning a dance in
February. I hope you'll be able to do your little bit in the
catering line—a few dozen savouries perhaps?"

"Er—yes, by all means."

"Oh, it would be a great help. When I think of all the people who are coming, my courage all but fails me. I've been planning it for weeks. So much to do. Decorating the Ellis-Parkers' grading shed. Seeing to the lighting effects. Arranging for a dance band to come out from town. The drinks and food . . . upon my word, I shall be a positive *wreck* when the time comes, won't I, Basil?"

"I'm sure you'll take it in your stride, my dear," said her husband.

"Surely you're not expected to cope with it all yourself?" I asked.

"No, no, it's meant to be all of us wives together, but you know what it is, one can't really rely on anyone. Three months is none too long with all I shall have to do. If the women here only had more spirit, perhaps we should be getting somewhere. I really can't imagine why I should take the whole thing upon my shoulders, but there you are, it's 'Mrs Harker, you will do this, won't you?' and, 'Mrs Harker, we do hope you'll see to that.' They do rather count on me, of course."

"How's Porky?" asked Pierre.

"Oh, my darling little Porky-pie! Well, actually we haven't seen him since yesterday, have we, Basil? Now you come to mention the little precious, I'd forgotten all about him. He does vanish sometimes, looking for a little lady friend, I fancy. I worry myself to distraction, but I simply haven't the time to go chasing after him in all the filthy native kraals. I daresay he'll turn up sometime."

"Talking of dogs," said Pierre, "my wife has informed me she is adopting a Kaffir dog which I have no doubt will turn out to be in the worst possible condition and quite untrainable!"

"Oh, the adorable little thing!" said Betty. "I can't wait

to see him. You will give him a good bath, won't you? Native dogs are quite revolting sometimes. These natives are so dirty. I had a native girl working in the kitchen once, though, and she used talcum powder on her baby's bottom. I thought that quite wonderful."

"I had a K-Kaffir dog once," contributed Basil, "when I was a bachelor."

"I should hope so, dear!"

"But he was a very c-c-c——"

"Clever dog. I'm sure he was, my dear. Now, Carol? A drop more sherry?"

"Thank you, no. We really must be going. I haven't done anything about dinner."

"But of course! I'm sure Pierre appreciates the lovely meals you give him, don't you, Pierre? I remember how often you used to come up and enjoy my little dishes. Talking of bachelors, we met *such* a nice young man the other day, Oliver Lindsay. He's the new assistant manager on Jimmy Wright's tobacco farm. He had the most delicious deep voice . . . and that particular way some men have of looking at women which I've always found quite irresistible. I believe his aunt is Lady Welk. Charming man. You liked him too, didn't you, Basil? If there's one thing Basil hates, it's pretence and insincerity."

\* \* \*

The following day I received an invitation from the Fawcetts, asking Pierre and me to dine with them that evening. "I do hope you will be able to come," the note said, "I know it is short notice, but we would so like to meet you, we have heard so much about you from Pierre, and my husband will be away most of next week on a tour with the N.C."

Half-way through the drowsy afternoon my kraal-bred pup was delivered. When his former owner had departed with half a crown clenched in his moist fist, I surveyed my acquisition, who sat outside the kitchen door and surveyed me. Though his body was in urgent need of soap and insect-powder, his eyes expressed a hope that had little to do with dirt or fleas. A dish was set before him and, with ears cocked and a ludicrously long tail curled stiffly in the air, he tasted bread and milk for the first time in his life.

The Africans never remove the tails of their puppies. Being beyond the age of tail-chopping, mine was to flaunt this hallmark of low breeding in the eyes of anyone who attempted to trace his ancestry; far from being embarrassed by his skeletal, flea-bitten appendage, he showed every sign of pride in its possession. Another singularity of the Kaffir dog is the long, sharply pointed nose. Even in his juvenescence this characteristic was apparent.

When Jennifer Burkitt appeared at the kitchen door on her daily informal call her eyebrows rose. "Where on earth did you pick up that thing?" she said with characteristic tact. The puppy lifted his peaky, milk-spattered face and looked at her. He licked his lips meditatively, then wiggled his tail and buried his offending nose once more in the bowl.

"I wonder what his ancestry is," I said, watching his stomach slowly distend. Jennifer said: "Extremely fishy." Conceding the truth of her opinion, I decided to call him Pilchard.

After licking the bowl clean, Pilchard recalled other problems and made a quick circle to track down a particularly irritating itch. But his haste outdid his equilibrium and he collapsed on the floor. Rising required considerable effort, unaccustomed as he was to his new dimensions. He managed to regain his legs, looked at the empty dish with a wrinkled forehead, and gave a squeaky bark. He placed a paw on the rim of the dish and sent it clattering on its side. The hint was a blatant one, but already tiny brown specks

were catapulting gaily about the kitchen floor, exploring new
territory.

Jennifer and I soaped his squirming body and dusted him
generously with flea-powder. On the completion of his toilet
he shook himself vigorously and swaggered about the grass.
The stirring whinny of Dick Turpin in the paddock caused a
momentary loss of composure, and he sat down heavily and
peered in the direction of the sound with one ear raised and
the tip of his tongue arrested between his black lips. He rose
and moved two steps toward the paddock, then paused to
look at me obliquely over his shoulder. After deliberating at
this angle for some moments, his eyes glassy, he turned back
and trotted importantly past us to the kitchen door, where he
sat on his haunches and smiled fatuously through the
gauze.

Having written all this, I realise that, just as dog-loving
appeals to the masses because it is a love without com-
plexities, so the temptation of dog-description writing appeals
because of the simplicities in which it revels. Why else the
repetition of cocked ears, wagging tails, lolling tongues and
flea-scratching?

Unlike Jennifer, Langton was quick to point out the best
in my puppy's conformation. "Is good, Nkosikaas, is good,"
he grunted and, holding the puppy firmly in one hand, he
caught its tail with the other and pulled it gently between its
kicking hind legs and back over the flank so that the tip
of the tail met the root. If a dog's tail was long enough to be
twisted round its hind leg and come back to touch its own
base, he explained at unnecessary length, the speed of the
dog was assured. Langton's expression clearly said, "What
more could one desire?" An African does not keep a dog as
a pet, but as a hunter; and to feed a dog—with such scraps
as they do feed them with—that is unable to outrun a rat in
the grass would be to invite the scorn of everyone.

Pierre, however, did not share Langton's enthusiasm. Hurrying barefoot through the house that evening after his bath, he stepped into a large, round puddle and swore horribly. The culprit sat sedately on a chair in the bedroom, watching me with the intentness of a child while I fidgeted at the dressing-table.

A minute later I was startled by a brutal note in my husband's voice: "Look! Look at the little devil now!" Pilchard lay on the floor with the remnants of a nylon stocking, chewing mouthfuls with quiet, sensual enjoyment. We made a concentrated rush and he rolled on to his back, one eye obscured by stocking and his taut stomach pleading mutely for pardon. Pierre caught him up and held him in one hand. "You lamentable specimen," he said, "an ill-formed mongrel from the tip of your nose to the tip of your ridiculous tail! *And* you'll eat us out of house and home, we who live on the oil of a smell rag as it is!" Pierre sometimes confused his idioms. "His mongrel ugliness is unimportant," I said. "I remember some lines from Spenser: '*Yet oft it falls that many a gentle mind dwells in deformed tabernacle drowned.*' Can't remember the rest."

It was regrettably late when we arrived at the Fawcetts' residence. "Frightfully sorry!" said Pierre with charming insouciance. "Carol bought a gentle-minded Kaffir dog puppy which is drowned, according to Spenser, in a deformed tabernacle." Mr Fawcett stood on the veranda with a lamp and laughed uncertainly. "Do come in."

We were introduced in semi-darkness and stepped into the drawing-room. In the bright light of several lamps our host stood blinking his round blue eyes. He was a very tall man, and his head seemed disproportionately small. His face was stamped with self-discipline and austerity, but nevertheless reminded one of a baby monkey.

"Do sit down," he said in an agreeably low-pitched voice, "I think Brenda will be here in a moment. She went to cajole our cook into special efforts. I fear he's inclined to daydream and requires constant spurring on, as it were. What will you have to drink?"

We were comfortably sunk into arm-chairs and therefore compelled to heave ourselves out of them again when Mrs Fawcett came in. She had a fruity smile—fruity is a very useful word with which to describe a certain kind of smile, but how did it ever come about? Why fruity?—and her voluptuous, self-indulgent expression contrasted strongly with her husband's asceticism.

"How do you do? Please don't get up. I've been trying vainly to instil a little enthusiasm into our wilting cook boy. Oh, no! I didn't mean that. You're not late at all. Had you come a minute earlier I should have been wallowing in the bath, and Michael battling gallantly with the lamps. A pink gin for me, Michael." She flopped into a chair and passed a plump hand wearily over her eyes. "Really, what a day it's been! I was struggling to finish an interminable mountain of washing this morning when in walked Michael and with true husbandly forethought said the irrigation officer was coming to lunch. There was I, up to my neck so to speak in soap-suds, and absolutely nothing whatever in the house that was remotely edible. He was a typical Rhodesian, too: dripping with perspiration and panting for beer!"

"Really, Brenda, that's a little unkind."

"Oh, well."

Pierre said: "The worst failing of typical Rhodesians, to my mind, is their fanatical passion for sport."

"*Vive le sport!*" said Brenda, flashing a smile at him. "I quite agree. I think a fate worse than death is to be forced to listen for hours on end to a Rhodesian boor slapping his big, hairy knees and extolling the virtues of 'rugger' and 'soccer'." She turned to me with an apologetic air: "I'm so sorry, I hope you're not a sport enthusiast?" I assured her that I had always regarded competitive sport as barbaric. Brenda smiled.

"Michael, do you remember Robin, that broad-shouldered young athlete in the Bahamas? You know, the one who had such a marked affection for me. His favourite pastime was violent exertion, regardless of heat. Even while he whispered sweet nothings in my ear, he flexed his muscles, and the greatest compliment he ever paid me was to say I showed more stamina at a party than any other female present!"

Pierre avoided my eyes. "Talking of parties," he said, "we were up at the store yesterday evening. Betty Harker, incidentally, was in tight grey silk, rather like a python that had swallowed something. Nothing fragile about her, is there? But, to return to the point, she spoke of a party she appears to be organising for February."

"We're all agog with excitement," said Michael dryly. "We shall suffer from anticipatory insomnia for weeks before the event."

Brenda said: "To be quite honest, I'm rather looking forward to it. This is such a ghastly little dump of a place. I *feel* like going gay. We used to have hectic parties almost every night in the Bahamas. I remember one night we'd all been imbibing rum punch of the most intoxicating sort, and I was sitting on some hefty male's knee—David, I think it was. He was crooning a wistful melody down the back of my neck, when an old admirer of mine suddenly turned nasty and rushed at us with a bull-like roar, wildly brandishing an empty curaçao bottle! There was I with my legs in the air, *screaming* for mercy, and Michael dancing about in the background, egging the brute on. Some young blood eventually came to my rescue, I think actually it was the redoubtable and brawny Robin."

"Quite untrue, Brenda! Whoever was egging him on, it wasn't me. I was taking advantage of the fracas by quietly consuming vast quantities of the aforementioned rum punch."

"How very callous!" I laughed.

"Not at all. I thought that, if matters came to a crisis, at least I should be well prepared to face the worst like a man!"

"Weren't you a little nervous that Brenda might be whisked away in the general mêlée?" asked Pierre.

"In the event of such a catastrophe I already had my eye on a particularly fascinating little Jewess," Michael said, nibbling an olive. Brenda's reply was dry: "Michael knows perfectly well that if he tried on anything like that I should be off like a flash with someone else!" I imagined Brenda flashing, like a kingfisher, after the hefty David and the broad-shouldered Robin, and said: "Apropos young bloods, etcetera, did Betty mention meeting someone called Oliver Lindsay to you? We heard all about him last night."

"I've met him myself," said Brenda, "and to be quite candid I thought he was perfectly sweet. Rather like a winsome teddy bear. Sophisticated and yet at the same time one could almost feel the physical power of the man. . . ."

"A great big hunk of masculine charm," said Michael with a mocking squeak.

"I thought you liked him too, Michael. Of course he has a rather special way with women. He could charm the proverbial bird off a tree with a quizzical twitch of his eyebrows."

"And they're perpetually twitching!" added Michael.

Pierre said: "Until yesterday I'd never heard of him and now he's become a household word." Brenda looked at me and said, "I do believe the men are a little jealous!"

"*L'amour, toujours l'amour,*" sighed Michael. "Yes, he is a recent development here. Most unfortunate!"

"Well, I fail to see why you're all becoming so disgustingly bellicose over the poor man," said Brenda with a girlish laugh. "We need someone like him to liven us up, don't you agree, Carol? Oh, no, but of course you're Newly Wed!" Her tone was faintly accusing and I felt rather guilty. Michael said: "I suggest we make a general exodus to the dining-room, if everyone has finished their drinks. There's *rognons sautés au vin blanc* for the entrée, and though I saw to the initial preparations myself, and left express instructions with the cook, I've a terrible suspicion he's *boiling* it!"

We sat down to candlelight. Candlelight is flattering, but its shadows gave such an odd and diabolical expression to our host's face that I have felt uneasy about my appearance in candlelight ever since. Following the entrée was a dish of highly seasoned fish and rice, for which Michael also took credit. "It's called *daube de poisson*," he said, "a Creole dish. Used to be a favourite of ours in the Bahamas, but I think we got the recipe from someone in Martinique. I grow chilli peppers specially for it. We produced the same thing the other night when we had the Fanshawes over to dinner. The old boy partook of the dish with undue gusto and suffered a violent attack of dyspepsia over coffee!"

Brenda said: "Daphne Fanshawe always displays such perfect poise and charm on these trying little occasions. I felt bound to excuse his discomfort on the grounds of the dish being too rich, but Daphne smiled at him with gentle reproach and said poor dear Harold never *could* resist our wonderful cuisine."

"He's an amusing character," said Michael, "a peculiar mixture. The fiery colonel type and yet rather Uriah Heepish with the richer farmers round here. He can be *sans peur et sans reproche* when it suits him, and at other times he can be devilish bad-mannered."

"Do you find him difficult to work with?" I asked. "I mean is he the sort of Native Commissioner described in novels who looks at you beneath beetling brows and barks out orders?"

"Well yes, he can be a little unnecessarily staccato as it were. Sort of Captain Fanshawe, D.S.O., D.F.C., style, but when I've really had a set-to with him he usually finds himself at a loss for words and resorts to what one might call the personal issue. His parting shot will be: 'Well anyway *your* cat kept us awake last night!' or something like that. With women he's rather *arch*. He was arch with our Belinda Storm when she peeped into the office to see Dutoit the other day."

"What an entrancing name! Who is our Belinda Storm?" said Pierre.

"She's Irma Dutoit's virgin sister. She's only been here a few days actually, left Mum in the Old Country and came out to stay with her married sister. Last chance Africa."

Brenda laughed delightedly and said: "Don't be so beastly. Unassailed virginity is not to be despised!"

"I should say the *alleged* virgin. On what grounds do you assume her to be one?" Pierre was determined to provoke them to further indiscretion.

"Her eyes betray it," said Michael, "two rolling marbles that have a glaze of decorum and chastity. I defy anyone to argue against her past, present and future virginity!"

"And yet she's called Belinda Storm!"

Over coffee and cointreau we were still speculating on the unsuitability of Miss Storm's name.

"I must say she's a very boisterous damosel," said Michael reflectively. "I believe she was a gymnastic mistress at a girl's school in Surrey. I have a vivid picture of her jerking her plump, pink thighs in a demonstration and gasping: 'Like this, girls! *One*, two, *one*, two!' . . . and all the innocents of the Lower Fourth, of course, had a violent crush on Miss Storm,

and practised sweaty feats for hours on end to win her praise.
And she would chide the weedy, bespectacled misfits in the
Lower Third: 'Oh, come, come, Ethel, we can't have you
drooping like that! One, two, *up*! Let's pretend we're great
big rubber balls, bouncing on the spring-board!' And when
she——"

"Michael, please! Spare us more," said Brenda im-
patiently. But he pursued the subject, in which he found a
strange fascination.

"I should imagine the hardened cynics of the Upper Fifth
saw through it all; at least one could hardly see through Miss
Storm's person—far too solid. But they said she was so re-
voltingly hearty and reduced the Storm to a damp patch—
that's it! They called Miss Storm Miss *Puddle*!"

Walking home in the starlight Pierre was unusually quiet
for a time, occasionally mumbling aloud to himself. At length
he said: "I've got it . . . um, wait a bit. Yes! Listen:

> Oliver was a teddy bear,
> And he got in a terrible muddle!
> He had a sophisticated air
> Till he met Belinda Puddle.
> She set his manly heart aflame,
> Then said: 'It's just a waste,
> The candle isn't worth the game,
> I'm really far too chaste!' "

## CHAPTER THREE

AN escort of five hundred men accompanied the small band of pioneers who were to form the first civilised community in Southern Rhodesia in the year 1890. These men were the first members of the Police of the British South Africa Company, of which Cecil Rhodes was the founder.

One can skim over the paragraph above with impatience, murmuring, "yes, yes, five hundred men, pioneers, 1890 and all that," and wondering why the bony finger of history should insert itself here at all. One could also read the paragraph—which is short enough—a second time and pause to reflect. The Union Jack that was unfurled against the hot blue sky —was it new and bright, with the fold creases of its journey still apparent? Or was it as torn and dusty as the uniforms of the tired troopers? The flag was first flown at Fort Victoria, now a town, then a plateau in the thorny wilderness where a stockade of stakes and branches was built under the direction of Colonel Pennefather, the officer in command. Protected with ditches and sandbags the little fortification was in a commanding position and a troop of police were detailed to garrison it. The pioneer column had trekked through the low veld and when the Fort Victoria stockade had been completed the men spent a week there, mending ragged, thorn-ripped clothing and resting the oxen and horses, many of which had died *en route* of exhaustion and horse-sickness. With a little effort one can feel the heat and the dust . . . hear the creak of the ox-carts, the clink of curb-chains and the liquid whistle of a bush-shrike. One can day-dream with armchair placidity on the discomforts, apprehensions and hopes in which the pioneer column moved.

Today the British South Africa Police number over a thousand European members and over two thousand Africans. They constitute the Territorial Police Force of Southern Rhodesia, District and Urban. New recruits receive comprehensive training: musketry; equitation; physical training; foot drill and riot drill—the latter term always conjures up an absurd picture in my mind of riotousness, a sort of holiday from the monotony of foot drill. The recruits are also given lectures which include medico-legal work, Common and Statute law and administration.

Though in rural districts their primary function is the detection and prevention of crime, and the maintaining of law and order among the Africans, they are also required to act as prosecutors at the local Magistrate's court; and the Force are sometimes called upon to assist the neighbouring Territories of Northern Rhodesia and Nyasaland in times of emergency.

The African members play a vital part as guides and interpreters for their own people. Indeed, three years as a district

member would provide newcomers to Rhodesia with a fairly
sound knowledge of the African and his environment—an
essential in a land where the European population of 211,000
is drastically outnumbered by an African community of
2,590,000.

Unlike the police force in the Union of South Africa, the
British South Africa Police of Rhodesia are sought with trust
by the African people; regarded by them as their protectors,
and not their suppressors.

The areas administered by one District Station are frequently the size of a county in England, and the native
reserves and European farms which they encompass are
constantly patrolled by European and African constables.
Where there are roads the Land-Rover is used, or the motor-
bike—my pet aversion. When the roads deteriorate into
paths, the patrols are carried out on horses, bicycles, or two
aching feet. Not only as interpreter is the African policeman
an essential to the patrol. In many cases, whether of theft,
witchcraft or murder, tribal superstitions and age-old African
customs play an integral part.

*        *        *

Six African constables stood smartly to attention on the
parade ground, each one impeccable in his stiff khaki drill
uniform, with brass buttons winking and flashing in the
morning sun. African Sergeant Marufu stood before them.
He expanded his chest and looked down the short length of
his broad nose with chilly hauteur.

"Parade. . . . Parade, SHUN!"

To me the commands which followed were hoarse and
meaningless. The culmination of their movements was a line
of motionless statues which he proceeded to inspect. I peered
over the grass fence and Pilchard took advantage of my
curiosity and gave my ankle a vicious nip, rolling on his

back and snorting with delight when I turned to admonish him.

" 'EFT, TIGHT, 'EFT, TIGHT!" Sergeant Marufu shouted in his deep voice and the African constables swung past me with faces rigid and eyes front.

"ABOOT TAHN!"

" 'EFT, TIGHT, 'EFT, TIGHT! . . . 'EFT, 'EFT, 'EFT!"

I returned to the house with Pilchard impeding my progress at every yard, and found Jennifer awaiting me on the veranda. She dimpled at me and said: "Been watching old Sergeant Marufu? He's an absolute treasure! I believe he's been in the Force for donkey's years. I came to ask if you'd like to come over to the office for tea this morning. All very irregular but they aren't particularly busy, so we might as well see something of our husbands while the going's good. Next thing they'll have a big store theft on their hands or something and we won't see them for days on end!"

Sergeant Billy Burkitt was a jovial man. Round-faced with a handlebar moustache and cerulean-blue eyes. Though an efficient policeman he had a breezy manner which left one with the impression that nothing would ever be of sufficient consequence to cause him perturbation; that he would regard pressure of work with equanimity, the irate public with amused tolerance, and reprimands from Headquarters with a good-humoured shrug of acceptance.

He shifted office chairs vaguely in our direction when we entered, and beamed at Jennifer while she poured the tea.

"We're embroiled in another rape case," he said cheerfully. "Silly business. African female Martha accuses one Mzuza of rape because he usually leaves a shilling under her pillow, so to speak, and this time he had the effrontery to drop a penny on the doorstep when he left." He chuckled and stirred his tea. "Doesn't merit a docket; no evidence to support her story."

"Have to do a spot of overtime today," said Pierre, nodding at the desk which was obscured by files and papers that covered it with alarming disorder, some slipping to the floor as he spoke. Billy glanced at the desk absentmindedly, fingering his moustache. "Get through that lot in no time, you mugwump!" he said.

The telephone jangled suddenly. Sergeant Burkitt left the large impression of his boot on one of the fallen papers as he stepped forward to lift the receiver.

"Hullo? Mrs Hennessy? Yes . . . yes, indeed, quite so. Er . . . I'm afraid it's not . . . yes, quite, most annoying, but I'm afraid that's. . . . Oh, I'm sure you must, most annoying, yes, but I'm afraid we . . . yes, of course you were, but Mrs Hennessy, I'm afraid that's not really a matter for the police at all. We . . . yes, I'm sure you were but I'm sorry, we can't really do much in a case like that. I'll get an African constable to look into the matter next time your area is patrolled. I'm very sorry, Mrs Hennessy. Good-bye." He replaced the receiver with noticeable relief and smiled ruefully.

"Mrs Hen. with ruffled feathers again because her cook boy was impertinent. Said he 'no work good because she shouting at him, all day she shouting'. Poor blighter!" Billy raised his voice in mimicry: "I cannot stand for such insolence, Mr Burkitt. We simply dare not let a native get *away* with such behaviour. You simply *must* do something about it at once. They'll get the upper hand in this country and *then* where will we be? You can't *do* anything? Well if this is Federation, all I can say is it's most unfortunate. Good-bye, *Sergeant* Burkitt!"

Pierre, who was at the window, turned and said: "Hullo,

Jimmy Wright's paying us a visit; looks like his jeep."
Brakes squealed and a puff of dust drifted across the road. A
moment later two men entered the office. The first was a tiny
man with a turtle-like neck. Small, wiry and wizened, and so
deeply tanned that had it not been for his keen blue eyes he
might have passed for an Indian.

"Well, well, look who's here!" said Billy. "Mrs de Choisy,
let me introduce Jimmy Wright. Best shot north of the
Limpopo!" Mr Wright whipped out a gnarled brown hand
and shook mine, painfully. He turned and jerked his thumb
at the man behind him. "Meet Oliver Lindsay. New bloke.
Come to do all my donkey work." His rasping laugh splut-
tered wheezily into a hacking smoker's cough.

"How do you do?" said Oliver Lindsay with raised eyebrows and a faint smile. He must have been six feet tall in his
socks—pale-yellow socks that harmonised with the suède
shoes and fawn-coloured corduroys, and the green spotted
scarf knotted loosely at his throat. His luxuriant black hair
had been coaxed into side whiskers, and the same freedom
of growth was encouraged at the nape of his neck, but his
moustache had been carefully trimmed and was not allowed
to trespass over his full lips.

"We goin' fishin'," said Jimmy Wright, pulling a crumpled
packet of cigarettes from the pocket of his khaki shirt.
"Thought I'd pop in an' tell you . . . bein' Crown Land. Have
to get out in the bundu and stretch me legs once in a while."
He turned to Pierre: "How's the old job? Crime tickin' over
nicely?"

"So, so," said Pierre. "Enough to keep the camp adequately
supplied with bandit labour."

"Bandits?" said Mr Lindsay. Pierre explained that African
prisoners in district stations are usually referred to as bandits
by the police—a friendly term.

Jimmy Wright twinkled at me. "Bandits! They see a poor

*munt** with his dog an' if the dog don't have a string to lead it by they bump him and haul the poor mug in an' make him do hard labour for the next six months!" Pierre cut into his rusty laugh: "Take a look at the poor mugs doing hard labour outside. They're given free board and lodging and there they are."

A small group of Africans were scattered over the patch of lawn that grew in front of the offices; they squatted on their heels in the sun, weeding. One hummed softly to himself, and a helmeted guard leant on his rifle, day-dreaming and wiping the flies from his shiny brown face. Jimmy bestowed a crafty wink on Mr Lindsay. "Can't fool us, eh?" he said. "Got a lot more breakin' up rocks somewhere behind the scenes till they drop dead on the job. Then they'll throw the carcasses to the vultures. Tough mob, these police guys!"

"If you were more polite, I'd offer you a cup of tea," said Billy. "As it is, I'll ignore you. Will you have some tea with us, Mr Lindsay?"

"I should love a cup, if it's not too much bother. I can't answer for my employer's prejudices, but I'm grateful that I don't have to suffer for them." He looked down at Jennifer and me with the smile that Mrs Harker had found quite irresistible, and moved forward to accept the proffered cup with a carefulness that emphasised his large frame.

"I've a kind heart and I'll relent," said Billy. "Have a cup, Jimmy? If you don't mind drinking out of the one I've been using?"

"Ta," said Jimmy.

Oliver smoothed his moustache lightly with his finger before taking a sip of tea. "By jove," he said, "it's hot, too! I'm favourably impressed with the B.S.A. Police. If I can be as successful in—er—certain other fields as you fellows appear

* *Munt.* Commonly used Rhodesian term derived from Shona; *munu:* man, person, object.

to have been, I may even offer my services as a new recruit!"
He regarded Jennifer and me once more with playful
significance.

"I'd better take care of this bloke," said Jimmy. "He's a
regular Don Jewan." Oliver put down his cup, placed an
unlit pipe between his teeth and folded his muscular arms.
His voice was tinged with condescension. "I should imagine
the B.S.A.P. know how to take care of their women, even if
they don't always get their man, hmm?" His broad shoulders
shook with soundless laughter that brought his agile eyebrows into play. "Dear me!" he said. "We must endeavour
to keep on the right side of the law." He bit his pipe-stem and
looked sideways at us, but his thoughts were elsewhere.
Flippancy was discarded and the vapid face became grave.
He hooked his thumbs into his belt and narrowed his eyes.

"I read Gunther's *Inside Africa* avidly before I left Home,"
he said, "and a certain passage in it, which rather surprised
me at the time, has just flashed across my mind. When he was
eulogising the Belgian policy in the Congo, and remarking
on the natives there being so much better treated, I believe he
said 'how refreshing it was, after the Rhodesias and the
Union,' to see Africans at work in various skilled trades,
etcetera, including traffic policemen. I think he concluded
the passage by saying with sarcasm: 'Imagine a Negro
policeman in Bulawayo!' Now apart from the incorrect term
'Negro' for an African or Bantu here, was he right? I feel
sure I've seen African policemen in Bulawayo, and in fact
throughout Rhodesia. I paid a brief visit to Lusaka before I
came here and, when a friend of mine took me to the airport
in his car, I distinctly remember being held up by an *African*
policeman on point-duty in Cairo Road. As a matter of fact,
I very nearly missed the damned plane. Was the fellow then
acting without the majesty of the law?"

Billy chuckled and Pierre looked sardonic. "Extraordinary

c

how many people only see what they want to see! But I expect that, on the tours he takes, the crammed-with-intelligent-observation type of tour, one's bound to overlook *something*! He overlooked the rush-hour traffic in Rhodes Avenue in Salisbury when hordes of schoolchildren cross every day under the guidance of *African* constables!"

I followed that up: "And if you find yourself pressing the accelerator too hard on the Blantyre-Limbe road in Nyasaland you'll have an *African* constable in a white crash helmet roar up beside you on his motor-bike and say: 'Speeding, Bwana!' "

Our chorus penetrated Oliver's amused complacency. "Dear me!" he said. "Then it was just another inaccuracy. I may as well have saved myself the boredom of ploughing through a serious book. Silly of me! Could have read the other thing. It had a wonderfully lurid jacket with lions and luscious blondes in leopard-skins. *True Stories of Darkest Africa*, or something like that."

"Hah! They're all the same!" Jimmy said equivocally. "C'mon, Oliver, don't want us pitchin' camp in the dark!" He hitched up his baggy shorts. "S'long, everybody. Ta for the tea."

Oliver included us all in a propitiatory smile. "I appreciated both the tea and the—um—charming company. Hope we haven't taken up too much of your valuable time. I trust you'll see more of me in the near future." A blast on the hooter outside caused him to raise an eyebrow. He moved toward the door with long, loose strides, and gave us a last, disarming smile over his shoulder. He was checked and all but swung completely round by the short sleeve of his shirt catching on the door handle with a sound of ripping cloth. Ejaculating faintly under his breath, he hurried out.

"Sophisticated teddy bear!" said Pierre, "I'd say a self-conscious, flopsy bunny."

Jimmy's jeep lurched down the road. I could see Oliver Lindsay through the rear window, flicking a comb through his hair.

We were all having third cups of luke-warm tea when we heard a scuffle on the steps outside, and an African constable appeared at the door. He said: "There is a lunatic outside, sir."

"Is he violent?" asked Billy.

"The men who have brought him say he try to escape, but is not violent, no, sir."

"Well, bring him in."

Jennifer smiled wryly. "This is where we wives fade away."

Outside an African was held by two others. His clothes were badly torn and his eyes seemed not to focus. Jennifer and I strolled down the gravel path, bordered with the regimental white-washed stones that bordered every path in the camp.

"What will they do with him?" I asked.

"Oh, question his escorts first to make sure it's not a frame-up. Ask who he is, where he comes from, and what he's done to make them say he's a loony. Find out how long he's been acting queer and so on. Then they'll keep him in a cell till the doctor comes on his weekly visit. If the doctor decides the boy *is* mad and certifies him, they'll send him to the asylum in Bulawayo under escort."

"Are lunatics often brought to the camp?"

"Well yes, usually in the hot season—October. Just a bit balmy, they often get over it. Sometimes they yell something awful at night in the cells when there's a bright moon. If they get terribly violent, the native orderly at the clinic gives them an injection to calm them down."

We stopped in the shade of an ancient flame tree, watching the yellow-bellied lizards that scuttled round the base of the trunk.

"I read somewhere about lunatics here in the old days," Jennifer mused, "before Europeans came to the country. Apparently some tribes used to send their mental cases out into the fever-ridden swamps. If they weren't taken by a crocodile or something, they were bound to get malaria. In certain types of mental affliction a high temperature restores the person to sanity . . . so if they survived the other hazards and recovered from the fever I presume they returned to the bosom of the family and lived happily ever after. Most of their treatments seemed to be kill-or-cure!"

We parted and when I reached the cottage I found a gang of jocund "bandits" weeding the drive. Pilchard, nearly wild with delight, was prancing between them. Nipping their most vulnerable parts and darting off again before they had time to turn. When he caught sight of me, he raced up and collided with my legs, tumbling head over heels. The prisoners bent assiduously over their work, hiding their smiles between their knees.

In the garden the morning sun slanted through the leaves, exposing their veins in a lemon-green X-ray. Little, chirping, blue wax-bills floated between the branches, touching down on twigs and vanishing again, perpetually restless. Unmoved by the vacillating wax-bills, a fat-bellied spider hung motionless on its silver web; if it was aware of the frantic gnat enmeshed below, it gave no sign. Had it been a human, I felt it would have been heavy-jowled, with drooping eyelids and a flaccid mouth.

But the weeds, the dying zinnias! . . . I called the bandits' guard. Soon the neglect became less apparent. Undergrowth was cleared. Enormous magenta drifts of bougainvillea blossoms that carpeted the earth and harboured a ghost-pale gecko were swept away. Thin-stalked, shrunken-headed zinnias were uprooted. With so much labour at my disposal, the formation of a landscape garden seemed a feasible proposition. With a half-formed image in my mind of a picture I had once seen of Prince Hotta's garden in Tokio, with its stone lanterns, and trees weeping over huge, tranquil lakes, and kimono patterns assembled under mists of wistaria and other features impracticable here, I said to the guard: "I want some large rocks." He came stiffly to attention and tried to look shrewd.

"I want them round the tree here, by the bird-bath."

"Yes, Nkosikaas."

He called the boys from their varied employments and herded them out of sight. I stood in the dappled light and planned the prospect. A hill here with craggy cliffs of nodular rock, and below . . . below I kept seeing Prince Hotta's vast shimmering lake. A very small grasshopper kicked itself across my bird-bath, tactfully reminding me that my plans must encompass a lake eleven inches in diameter. I heard a series of low grunts and turned to see a line of bandits hurrying toward me, each clutching a boulder. The guard stumped along beside them, his round face hopeful.

"Wait!" I called. "Where did they get those stones from?"

"This stones are not wanted, Nkosikaas," he answered soothingly. "They have been throwed away. I find them under a tree behind the prison."

"Well, I'm afraid you will have to have them all taken back to the tree behind the prison," I said regretfully. Every rock had, on some earlier occasion, been carefully and thickly white-washed.

But I found them at length, my rugged grey boulders. They were hidden by the brittle grass, barely five yards from the garden boundary. The bandits dropped them with reverberating thuds and stood back panting. Then the rocks had to be half-buried for the natural effect. The whole undertaking became increasingly bewildering to the bandits and their guard. No one was quite certain of the outcome.

Pilchard scratched at the loose earth in a frenzy, periodically breaking off to plunge about the lawn in yapping circles, with ears laid back and long tail bouncing. When eventually the foundations of my landscape were laid, I tried to visualise the ultimate effect. The formality of the central bed that awaited flowers seemed unrelated to the weather-beaten rocks; they needed a link—stepping-stones would suit admirably. Meandering in a wide curve across the grass, they would create the desired impression of rusticity. I marked off the drunken course with pegs and gave explicit instructions.

I returned later to find the stones had been laid. The guard had taken pity on my faulty vision and corrected the irregularity of the line. My roving pegs had been compassionately removed. Twelve round stepping-stones took the shortest route from the bird-bath to the flower-bed, a precise and urban path. The less advanced African is not yet able to appreciate the modified landscapes of Japanese gardening; yet, paradoxically, to employ an African in a garden of any formality is a hazardous undertaking. Their conception of a straight line is very flexible.

Pierre came up behind me and laughed. "*Ça fait rien!*" he said. "Make them change it tomorrow. But—darling, did you mean them to do *that*?" He was looking at the palm. The curving fronds would not brush faint herringbone lines on the dust when the wind blew again. A zealous bandit had clipped off the lower half of every frond with painstaking care to keep them of even length. The palm bore a remarkable resemblance to a monk's tonsure.

\*    \*    \*

Several branches of the church were represented in the Dzokuti district. The word of the Gospel was spread among the heathen, accepted with fervour or with tolerance; seldom rejected, and often fortuitously linked with deep-rooted superstitions, for to backward people religion and super-stition are very much akin.

But even when the seed was sown on barren ground, its husk was of benefit. The clinical work and school-teaching undertaken by the missionaries were appreciated by the Africans, in their phlegmatic manner.

The majority of the missionaries were from the States. They told one, with honest American candour, that they had been "born anew". Their naïveté and singleness of purpose are more to be admired than mocked, because few people are so sincere. And if they were ingenuous in their approach it was in keeping with their work, for preachers should never resort to guile. If they had a fault it was dogmatism.

One hot afternoon an African constable knocked at the back door with a message from Pierre: "Darling I'm doing radio can you give Lewis tea?" The line appeared to have been written in great haste and composed by a preoccupied mind.

Though convinced that police wives are not normally called upon to entertain African constables to tea, I never-theless felt it prudent to ascertain the message-bearer's name. But even as he smilingly informed me that his name was Mushaba, I heard a knock on the front door. Calling to Langton to set a tea-tray for two, I hurried through the house. Standing diffidently outside was a short, bandy-legged man in khaki with a homely, sunburnt face. He re-moved his pith helmet and it left its impression in red across his damp forehead.

"Mrs de Choisy? Pleased to meet you. My name's Lewis, Lewis T. Brocken." He spoke with a broad American accent and was without doubt a missionary.

In features Lewis T. Brocken was an ugly man, but he had a most engaging manner. He talked of his wife, Maryanne, and their two little daughters, Joanne and Marylou. When Langton came in with the tea, Lewis addressed him in fluent Shona.

"They give us three months to learn the lingo," he said, when Langton had left the room. "Boy! You sure have to put plenty work into those three months!"

Some missionary workers are complacent on the effect of their preaching, others bitter at the apathy they encounter. Lewis Brocken was of the former. His face glowed with enthusiasm when he spoke of his work, and described the mission. I could see the scattered buildings, thatched and white-washed; the bare swept earth reflecting the scorching sun; the mud-floored structure that served as chapel and schoolroom, where young Africans droned their lessons on weekdays and sang "Onward, Christian Soldiers!" on drowsy Sunday mornings; and the well-worn footpath that led a constant stream of patients to the little white-washed clinic, with sore eyes, cut feet, pneumonia, constipation, snake-bites, malaria, and toothache.

Following that trend of conversation we inevitably stumbled upon religion. Lewis Brocken felt compelled to edify and justify. His honest, beseeching eyes embarrassed me, but on Adam and Eve I was obstinate.

"I can't be persuaded that man underwent no evolution but simply strolled into the world—a bearded lotus-eater, temporarily unclothed," I said with unnecessary vehemence. Lewis Brocken smiled, but his eyes remained sober.

"That is just exactly what happened, and that is why it is all so wonderful," he said earnestly. "Say, you only need to look out at the trees and sunlight and birds and all—isn't that a miracle? All created by God from nothing. And if He is capable of creating all that beauty outside, well, I don't question His ability to put man on earth, formed as he is today."

"I don't allow it to be an impossibility," I argued, "but the very manner in which the world was evolved, the imperceptible growth from heat and gas to life, is an unfathomable miracle. And the life that eventually became man as we know him today is a miracle that conforms with the whole Creation. I find it unnecessary to believe that he landed on Earth formed as he is today, for I think he grew *with* the world, and the degrees of his growth are more wonderful than your vision of his sudden arrival."

Brocken fiddled with his helmet and pursed his lips. His tone was obdurate. "You oughta read your Bible, Mrs de Choisy, and you wouldn't talk about man's arrival. In the Book of Genesis the words are there for all men to read: 'And the Lord God formed man of the dust of the ground, and breathed into his nostrils the breath of life; and man became a living soul.' A simple statement of fact, but a miracle. The Bible never exaggerates and you can't tell me it's wrong. The Bible don't tell lies either!"

"Not wrong," I said, "and not exaggerated, but over-simplified for the people of the days in which it was written. They wouldn't have been able to comprehend a scientific explanation. But the simplified version is as true as the scientific. Take the words, 'formed man of the dust of the ground'. The beginning of life was very similar—living cells expanding and multiplying, and different conditions and elements causing diversified forms of life. Science doesn't deny, it explains. The length of time taken to form man of the dust of the ground must be our argument, and nowhere in Genesis does one find any mention of time——"

Lewis interrupted: "You forget it was the evening of the sixth day," he said; "on the seventh day the work was ended. Man was made in God's image, and I can't see God in the form of a hairy ape." We both smiled at his unintentional blasphemy. I said: "But what is the image of man? His soul or his body? In either case, one must remember that with Creation a thousand years become a fleeting moment, and with the passing centuries it's probable that man will become more God-like, if he is permitted to survive, both in body and soul. One can hardly claim that his soul has reached perfection today and, besides finding it a little conceited to say that we resemble Him physically, I see no reason why He should be burdened with a body at all and think it highly unlikely that He is."

I showed him lines from Akenside's "Pleasures of the Imagination".

> His parent hand,
> From the mute shell-fish gasping on the shore,
> To men, to angels, to celestial minds,
> Forever leads the generations on
> To higher scenes of being; while supplied
> From day to day with his enlivening breath,
> Inferior orders in succession rise
> To fill the void below.

"Yeah, well that's . . . that's very good poetry," said Lewis, "but there's no getting away from the true Bible story. And what does science say about the existence of Satan? I believe in the existence of Satan and he's mighty powerful."

Science and I had no answer. I thought irrationally of two lines from "David and Bethsabe" written in 1599 by someone whose name always eludes me, though the lines themselves have a lasting freshness, almost amounting to pantheism:

> God, in the whizzing of a pleasant wind,
> Shall march upon the tops of mulberry trees. . . .

Despite the futility of our discussion, curiosity prompted

me to read the Book of Genesis directly Lewis Brocken had departed. When I did so, I could only regret that I was so unfamiliar with the prose of the Bible.

Soon after this discourse upon the origin of man, Pierre and I encountered a Serpent in our garage—a flimsy structure of reeds—though at the time I did not recall the Original Sin and the Garden of Eden as Lewis Brocken would have desired, but was instead reminded of the old proverb: "*Africa semper aliquid monstri parit*"—Africa is always bringing forth something monstrous.

The snake, a black-necked cobra, froze into immobility when our shadows fell across it, and fixed us with its evil, cold little eyes.

"*Nyoka!* Snake! Buyisa lo stick!" yelled Pierre. Langton flung open the kitchen door, clutching a broom, an expression of unwarranted terror distorting the mildness of his features. He offered the broom at arm's length and retreated some twenty yards.

At the first stroke of the broom handle, the cobra—to use Brenda Fawcett's expression—recoiled in horror. Hissing, it unfolded its length and slid to the far corner of the shed where it pressed blindly against the wall, flinching at the blows that followed its retreat. Its head rose in a desperate attempt to find a gap between the reeds; its tongue quivered out in mute warning of the twin needles of danger that hung within.

Reluctant to attack, and occupied only with the instinct to escape, it proved an easy victim in the confines of three walls. Crippled and partially disembowelled, it still clung to life and struggled weakly to escape; and this most deadly reptile evoked my unwilling pity, for what was it after all but another living thing, pathetically maimed. When of necessity one ends a life—whether of mosquito, scorpion or caterpillar—

one feels an apology is called for. Whether it is a salve to one's conscience, an apology to the creature, or an appeal to the Creator I have never stopped to consider.

But if small caterpillars yield with reproachful suddenness, the cobra does not. Pierre bent forward with the broom handle for the *coup de grâce*, then astonished me by flinging the broom to the winds before delivering the final blow, and shouting: "Ugh! Oh God, my eyes!" Black-necked cobras have the ability to spit from the ground without raising their heads, and their aim is remarkably accurate.

Avenged and forgotten, the cobra was left to die while I guided Pierre to the house. His eyes were tightly closed, the muscles contracted, and his face tense with pain.

"Don't worry, darling! The pain will go, it'll be all right," I said, but the words were not calm. The sound of them came back to me in a thin thread, unreal, beating against my ear-drums with panic, echoed in the beating of my heart. *Can he go blind?*

I snatched at a tiny bottle of eye-drops on the bathroom shelf.

"What are you doing?" Pierre's voice seemed far away.

"Eye-drops," I said firmly. "They'll wash the poison out." *Will he go blind? Never see me . . . never see anything again? Oh heavens, he can't! Not like this!*

"Keep still, darling, I must get your eyes open." My hand shook with the bottle-stopper that had turned to a dancing point of light in the wet mist of my own eyes. The eye-drops trickled ineffectively down Pierre's chin. He clenched his hands. "Couldn't you phone the doctor?" he said with a mixture of patience and irritation, and sweet reason came back to me.

The doctor's slow voice, over forty miles away, was reassuringly expressionless. "Milk, Mrs de Choisy. Just keep on bathing his eyes with milk. Neutralises the acid you see, and takes the pain away. He'll be all right in a day or so, if he rests his eyes and keeps them out of the glare. They'll be all right; just you keep on bathing them with milk."

I was willing to buy out a dairy. Half an hour later, when my fingers were steady and Pierre's face milk-stained but relaxed, we heard hesitant voices outside. I went to the door and found Langton, saucer-eyed. With him was the local African clinic orderly, one Elias Madzamba, in his clean white shirt, and equipped with tourniquet, syringe, needles and phials of anti-venene serum, swabs of cotton wool, a bottle of antiseptic, a kidney bowl—and a keen delight in the dramatic situation.

## CHAPTER FOUR

DUST, powder-white, rolled thickly behind the car as we drove through Dzokuti one hot afternoon. We had been invited to tea by the new Land Development officer and his wife.

Flanking the narrow drive that led to the house were weary poinsettias. "Having grown this much," they seemed to say, "what more can be expected of us?" And they waited there, listless and depressed, like a queue of people who hope for any diversion to allay their boredom.

We drew up before the house and as I alighted from the car I perceived a large, plump-faced young woman peering at us through parted lace curtains. The curtains were hurriedly drawn together and a moment later she flung open the front door and gave us a breathless welcome.

"Hullo! Hullo! How do you do? Come in, come in. My name's Belinda, Belinda Storm. I'm Irma's sister. She's still dressing, she got a ladder in her stocking and had to change them!" Upon this last assertion, which was addressed to me in a tone of feminine confidence, she burst into falsetto

76

giggles. Still giggling, she shepherded us up the steps. Pierre whispered: "Hoff, hoff, a horralump!" as he followed close behind me.

Miss Storm moved awkwardly about the small drawing-room, plumping cushions and commanding us to "Sit down! Do sit down!" She opened a box of cigarettes, and in the process of offering them spilt several on the carpet. "Clumsy little me!"

Pierre helped her to retrieve them, and as she rose, flushed and slightly dishevelled, Mrs Dutoit entered the room. Irma Dutoit was small and birdlike. Her face resembled an apple —not the kind that is rosy red, but one that has been kept in storage and is consequently tart and slightly wrinkled. Her voice held the suspicion of a whine.

"I can't imagine why John's so long," she said. "See if the kettle's boiling, will you, Belle?"

"Of course!" Miss Storm crossed the room with a bounce. She collided at the door with a man who was about to come in, and her exit was made in a confusion of gusty laughter.

"G'morning," said Mr Dutoit, and sank into an armchair. "How do you like this Godforsaken little dump after the hot stuff in Salisbury?"

"I've found it very pleasant so far," I replied, wondering what the hot stuff in Salisbury might entail. The door was kicked ajar to the sound of rattling tea-cups, and Miss Storm bore in a laden tray. "Stay where you are, everyone!" she whinnied, "I'm doing the tea."

"I believe you haven't been here very long yourselves?" I asked Mrs Dutoit. But she was frowning at the tea-tray and seemed unaware of my question.

"That tray hasn't been cleaned properly!" she exclaimed. "Really these wretched boys are impossible. Can't trust them for a minute. And this is the third cook boy I've had since we got here. Disgusting, filthy creatures, they all need a good box on the ears!"

Mr Dutoit looked sullen, and muttered: "Ag, shut up! You go on and on." Miss Storm said loudly: "Have some cake? Or a cream scone?"

When we were all provided with tea, and sat with cups balanced precariously upon our knees and rounds of adhesive scone clutched between our fingers, I took advantage of the lull to examine the room.

The colour contrasts seemed a little uncertain, and the haphazard disposal of the furniture betrayed a complete indifference to comfort. Above the fireplace hung a landscape painting, a defiantly vivid sunset. On either side were thick china wall-plates, one depicting in relief an English cottage scene and the other a remarkably blue Victoria Falls. Delicacy had not been the aim of the designer. I was both repelled and fascinated by the array of ornaments on the mantelpiece. A six-inch nude in brass; an antelope carved in wood, with one horn broken and a missing leg; a Christmas card, warped and dusty; a blank-faced china dog. . . .

Mrs Dutoit smiled for the first time. "You like my little scotty? I bought him in Barnstaple . . . I think . . . or was it Bideford now? D'you remember, Belle? Barnstaple! That's right. I never let anyone else dust him. Come here, my sweetheart, and have some cake!"

I was startled, but discovered that her eyes had moved to a window, where they met those of a small girl in pig-tails. The smudged face vanished and reappeared at the door. Mr Dutoit's features relaxed into a smile.

"Come in, Angy-Pangy, there's a good girl!"

The child pouted and stalked into the room, where she stood in the centre of the carpet and eyed Pierre and me with marked aversion. Mrs Dutoit was busy cutting cake, and her sister stretched her plump arms toward her niece.

"Come along, Angela, say good morning to Mr and Mrs de Choisy! Oh fie! She's bashful. Never mind, there's a lovely big piece of cake your Mummy's cutting you!"

"Don't want it."

"Oh, Angy? Lovely cake with icing? Then have a scone?"

"Gimme a scone."

"Here you are, pet, you choose one."

Angela extended an unclean forefinger, removed the cream from a scone, and transferred it thoughtfully to her tongue. She repeated the operation on others, until gently reprimanded, whereupon she filled her mouth entirely with a scone and entertained herself and her parents by attempting to break her previous silence with speech, which was necessarily rendered incoherent, and caused her to expel the greater part of her scone, partially masticated, upon the floor.

"Now run along and play, kitten, there's my little angel!"

The advent of Angela released her parents from restraint. Their daughter became the focal point of conversation for a considerable period, and a subject to be recalled with relief when others failed. There was always some fresh remembrance of Angela's sweet little sayings and Angela's captivating ways.

Belinda Storm was a willing participant in the memories. Her preoccupation with the tea had given me little time to observe her. Now that she sat beside me on the sofa I was able to study her features and mannerisms, and found her boisterousness oddly engaging. When she laughed, her eyes disappeared; the rubber-like moulding of her face seemed to quiver and sag as a jelly might flounder if too hastily agitated. And she was seldom serious. Though in her middle thirties, she termed her speech with the simplicity of a child; but the want of consistency and perception in her conversation was amply compensated by her energy, and the sofa we shared

creaked beneath the impact. If Milton saw another vision,
his words were nevertheless admirably suited:

> . . . Jest and youthful jollity,
> Quips and cranks and wanton wiles,
> Nods and becks and wreathèd smiles. . . .

But wanton wiles . . . no, her wiles were certainly not
wanton; her innocence was uncontestable.

When a group of people are drawn together more by
courteous necessity than mutual desire, conversation is inclined to flow along directed lines, like water. In irrigating
vegetables, a gardener must seal the main furrow with his
hoe before coaxing the water into other channels. Thus, with
the utmost delicacy and tact, Pierre finally succeeded in
drawing the subject of little Angela to a close and opening
up new lines of thought, and Angela was supplanted by
politics and the Federation.

Mr Dutoit was in sympathy with the policies of South
Africa.

"Keep the bloody niggers under your thumb. What's all
this business about education, hey? They on'y want to learn
to count so they can own a store an' fleece their own black
brothers. Whadda they do with the profits? Man, they'll buy
a dirty great car to flash around the countryside and turn it
over in a ditch. I'd like to see one of these monkeys shoved
into a job where he had to use his brains! Man, they got the
right ideas down there in the Union—they don't let these
black apes get any ideas of equality!"

Africans can be exasperating. Even the best African ser-
vant, despite his pleasing tendency to whistle and sing over
his work, has little or no sense of responsibility. Like most
Rhodesian housewives, I am quite ready to spend a few
minutes enumerating the faults of my cook with increasing
bitterness. But Mr Dutoit's expressions were irritating, and

even though Langton *did* get drunk, and burn the meat, and wipe the kitchen floor with a dish cloth if no other rag was at hand, I could not agree that they had the right ideas down there in the Union.

"But surely," I protested, "there are a great many Africans who hold positions requiring intelligence. And among these 'black apes' whom you feel to be so inferior to the Afrikaans who govern them, there have been idealists who have educated themselves in order to benefit their own race. What about the Zulu, John Langalibalele Dube? He was born a chief's son, but he renounced all claims to chieftainship and after an education in Natal and America he founded the Ohlange Institute, an educational institute with industrial departments; and he founded one of the first Bantu newspapers, *Ilanga Lase Natal*. What about Sol Plaatje of the Bechuana who translated some of Shakespeare's plays into his own language; and the Rev. Dr Rubusana, who translated the Bible into Xhosa? These achievements shouldn't be erased by the more recent vituperations of Dr Hastings Banda."

Irma Dutoit roused herself to a degree of vehemence of which I had felt her incapable, and declared that the Federation would become a Black state in no time at all.

"Another Kwame Nkrumah will rule us all, and bring out a white woman for his wife, what's more. You see if he doesn't!"

I was awed by her superior knowledge, and conceded that the racial problems of the country which to me indicated such delicate tangles, such tautly knotted problems, must perforce appear to her, a newcomer, in so simple a light as to present no difficulty at all. Yet with all the experience she had garnered in her spinster days at Barnstaple she could offer us no definite solution to the inevitability of a Black state.

Her sister adopted a more cheerful approach, suggesting that if half the Federation's black population were sent to England and an equal number of English emigrants transported to the Federation things would be evened up as it were, and everyone would be happy. On this brighter view we made our departure, being entreated by the Dutoits to repeat our visit, though their daughter watched us malevolently through the poinsettias and poked her tongue out as we drove away

*       *       *

In mid-November came the first heavy rain of the season. For five months soft cumulus clouds had strayed fruitlessly, like melting marshmallows, across the pale, unending stretch of sky. Now they assembled and moved with a ponderous importance, till their burden could be withheld no longer. A breeze sifted the sultry air and shook limp leaves into a trembling dance. Tree-frogs called rapturously to the barking thunder. The first hard drops bounced on our tin roof and splattered on the dusty paths.

All the morning with persistent and elfin monotony a piccanin had played his reed flute behind the banana palms. The thin thread of sound broke off abruptly, and a moment later the rain came down with a roar that filled me with a pagan madness—a desire to sing savage songs above the pounding on the roof, to rush about Dzokuti in wild abandon, splashing through the cocoa-coloured rivers that raced beside the road, and stamping over the sodden grass. But such freedom is one of the few pleasures of childhood—and childhood holds more pleasure in retrospect than ever it had at the time. We must stifle these peculiar desires and conform to our self-imposed standards of decorum. Eccentricity is only acceptable when it is an orthodox eccentricity like wearing badly darned tweeds, keeping sixteen dogs, and being curt with one's neighbours. It would never do to run panting past the Native Commissioner's offices with streaming hair and soaked dress, while that worthy gentleman corrected his clerk's errors and frowned at the idea of muddying his shoes when he went home for his lunch.

I slid barefoot around the garden, over steaming earth and under shining leaves, and thought of the lovely words of the Chinese poet, Su Tung-P'o:

> So I dance with my limpid shadow
> As if I were no longer on earth.

But I slipped heavily in the mud and returned to earth—not limpidly.

White spears of lightning veined the sky with patterns that vanished before they could be traced, yet left the jagged impression dancing on one's eyeballs. The Africans have a vivid idiom: *"Runji rusingapfumi nguo, rwaivetera kupfuma pasi"*— The needle which does not sew cloth but has to sew beneath. Implying that God reveals Himself in lightning as a needle which unites heaven and earth.

The Africans are fond of riddles. I endeavoured to extract one from Langton and, after wriggling shyly and wiping his mouth, he finally intoned: *"Zimbgha ra Makashu rinodhla rivete."*

"What does that mean, Langton?"

"That meaning this big dog of Makashu, him eating but him lying down same time."

The answer to that one was "duvu", a conical fish-trap made of reeds which is submerged in rivers so that the open mouth faces upstream, and hence likened to a dog that eats while lying down.

I rather unkindly pointed out that Langton was a riddle himself in his ability to sleep while standing up, for I had frequently surprised him dozing over the stove, or leaning heavily upon the ironing board with mouth half-open and eyes half-closed.

Langton possessed other traits, which, though in no way remarkable in a cook, were so numerously displayed in one person as to set him apart from the common cooks of Dzokuti, each of whom could boast but few faults and vices in comparison.

From Saturday afternoon till the grey dawn of Monday morning Langton remained obliviously intoxicated. We proposed that this complete absence over weekends should be compensated by his sober presence throughout the day during the week, depriving him of the customary afternoon off. He accepted our decision with dignity.

Langton was the father of many children; the majority were illegitimate but they accepted, nevertheless, the bounty of our kitchen. Loaves of bread diminished with extraordinary rapidity, as did anything else that was not kept under lock and key. His large family were never in evidence during the day. It was at night that low murmuring, faint scuffling and smothered laughter softly rose and fell from the candle-lit kitchen while we dined. If we opened the living-room door, small phantom forms glided across the pencil of light and melted in the dark.

Utterly unable to discern dust, Langton's housework was of the most cursory nature. If I unbent sufficiently to draw a simple face with my finger-tip on the window-sill or the surface of a table, the humour of the situation would reduce him to weak chuckles for the remainder of the day, and the purport of my action lost its significance.

He implored me to buy him a white chef's cap—"Same like that boy him cook for missus Fansher". No doubt the cap gave him the requisite prestige among his acquaintance. Perched so very rakishly over one eye as to impair his vision, its starched perfection sat incongruously on so dismal a chef. Hollow chest, ill posture and chronic dejection were Langton's characteristics. This lugubrious countenance, with a cigarette of damply rolled newspaper hanging from the lips, did nothing to enhance his headgear; and the impressive headgear did nothing to improve his incompetence as cook. Toast was unfailingly burnt, and rice congealed. Meat would shrivel to cinders while he day-dreamed, and milk boil over —hissing about the stove like an aggravated sigh.

However, he had one redeeming quality. He washed Pierre's uniform and starched the khaki drill till it buckled like varnished cardboard. With tuneless, joyless humming, he polished boots till they reflected his own woebegone face; brass buttons were rubbed with unlimited patience into winking lights. By these services was the regular arrival of his monthly pay ensured.

\* \* \*

"The niceties of etiquette are not strictly observed among the locals," said Pierre one day. "Whenever I'm out on patrol the farmers entreat me to 'bring your wife out, we'd *love* to meet her!' I very much doubt if they'll call on you but they'll all be frightfully hurt if you fail to call on *them*!"

Consequently we set out one sparkling Sunday morning to pay our respects to the Goldmans. The most direct route to their farm took one through several miles of native reserve territory.

The rain had coaxed scores of wild flowers to unveil their fragile faces: little scarlet Rhodesian pimpernels lifted their chins buoyantly, and trailing convolvulus scattered its pale lavender trumpets over the earth; bright yellow daisies bobbed in the sun; purple blossoms starred the rampageous apples of Sodom and, borne on proud stems in their maroon and yellow livery, the full-lipped flowers of Ngulula, the wasp-

orchid, swung in the breeze. As though drunk with the sudden
choice of colour, butterflies dithered about in confusion. Sun-
flecked Painted Ladies aired themselves, still wrinkled from
the chrysalis and more tardy in testing their new-found freedom than the tiny, ecstatically darting Common Blue. And
betrothed Cabbage Whites rose erratically on pristine,
amorous wings.

Spring in Rhodesia is hustled and obscure—new shoots
hidden in dusty grass; seedlings heaving up the hard baked
earth with their bent necks; *mfuti* trees with their new leaves
tight sheathed in pink silk. The only signs of spring that refused to be hustled and were far from obscure were the
young leaves shaken out by the *msasa* trees: a tender scale
ranging from palest cider to glowing Burgundy.

The rutted road took us past native kraals where the surrounding bush was denuded by their straying goats, and the
piccanins ran shrieking with delight behind the car, their
laughing, dirty faces half-concealed in fog-like billows of
dust.

It is an uphill struggle to prevent Africans from allowing
their cattle and goats to over-graze the land to the last blade
of grass, and when we left the native reserve and came into
the farming area the difference in the surrounding vegetation
was immediately apparent.

To either side of the sandy white road the bundu spread,
more grey than green, varied by the rosy brown and parch-
ment of ploughed land. Blue hills broke the horizon, range
upon range unfolding till they merged with the sky. The land
of tobacco . . . of burning sun and flooded rivers; spiced with
new endeavour and peppered with the problems of race;
sweetened with the old heritage of freedom and soured with
the delusions of spoon-fed emigrants. But the condiments are
stirred on the surface, unable to penetrate the enigmatic core.

Where England dimples in her yielding green, Africa basks independent in her ochre brown. Where England appeals for protection, Africa shrugs an indifferent shoulder.

"The Goldmans are as rich as Croesus," said Pierre; "they live in an enormous house and own a fleet of cars. But there the outward show of the Goldman fortune ends; they've never been to Europe, although they could afford to go every year. They prefer to drive down to Durban to sample the sago puddings of the Seaview Hotel, and Bert plods over the golf links while Dolly dozes on the esplanade."

We turned at a battered sign marked "B. Goldman— *Msasa*". The narrow farm track led us several miles farther before we saw any sign of habitation, then the tall brick tobacco barns appeared. We drove past numerous sheds and into a yard that seemed to be filled with tractors, cars, jeeps and lorries. There was no formal drive to the Goldman family seat; in fact, no approach at all that could be made in a car, and we had to leave our little Anglia, looking very out of place and rather prim, among the motley collection of farm vehicles.

As we walked toward the house, marvelling at its bleak magnificence, we were diverted by a shrill hail behind us.

Her hair stood out in fuzzy disorder, the hem of her dress was sufficiently uneven to reveal the torn lace of her petti-coat, and her proportions could be described as nothing less than massive. Yet her round, coarse-featured face glowed with a friendliness and warmth that could be copied to advantage by many an apathetic hostess, and her pleasure at our arrival was undisguised by the sophisticated banalities commonly adopted when receiving guests. She looked me over with a frank curiosity and turned to Pierre:

"Hell! Why'd you take so long to show us your new bride, you bastard? Anyway, now you're here, come in for a drink.

Bert'll be inside, squatting over the radio as usual, listening to the cricket."

The wide veranda was temptingly cool but Dolly Goldman led us firmly into the drawing-room. Her husband was, as she predicted, huddled deep in an armchair, listening to a sport commentary with a beer-mug clenched in his hand. As we entered the room we were informed by the jubilant voice of the commentator that a certain Mr Grimbleby had just bowled superbly and in consequence a certain Mr Putney was caught with his leg before the wicket, which sounded extremely awkward and painful.

My knowledge of cricket is very slight but I concluded that Mr Putney could not have been seriously injured, for if he were the rejoicings of the commentator would be very unseemly; apart from that, Bert Goldman's heavy, pugilistic face was stamped with such benevolence that delight in another's misfortune would be quite out of keeping with his apparently amiable nature.

"Bert, Pierre and Carol are here!" Dolly was forced to raise her voice above the excited cries of the commentator. "Turn that damn thing off and be sociable!" she bellowed. Bert turned slowly, as if in a trance, but when he perceived us he rose with outstretched hand, and greeted us with an exuberant bellow that reverberated through the house.

"So this is Carol, hey? Pleased to meet you. What'll you drink? Beer, gin, whisky, vermouth?"

So early in the morning I should have infinitely preferred tea, but one is taught to submit without flinching to any odd suggestion that one's host may make in his efforts to be hospitable. I found myself grasping a tankard of foaming beer.

"How's the tobacco?" asked Pierre conversationally, as he sank beside Dolly on the sofa. Bert drew the back of his hand across his mouth and groped for a cigarette.

"O.K. so far," he shouted. "Seed beds pretty healthy. Starting to plant out. Put in about ten acres, but it's mighty dry still. The rain's missed us up to now."

Dolly took a long draught from her beer mug. "Feel like a weed in a drought myself," she said, blowing out her cheeks and expelling her breath like a deflating balloon. Bert surreptitiously turned on the wireless, reducing the volume so that the ebullient sport commentator sounded like a bee droning in the distance. He inclined his head in the direction of the sound, keeping a wary eye on Dolly.

"What a comfortable sofa this is!" remarked Pierre. On the strength of his mild observation all further conversation on our part was reduced to exclamatory punctuations to Dolly's enthusiastic evaluation of the room's furnishings.

"Got it at Newell's with the armchairs, cost us a hundred, without the upholstering. That was another seventy odd. The curtains came to seventy-five, but they were just the right colour, so what could I do? That bloody radiogram Bert's drooling over was damn near two hundred—waste of money if you want my personal opinion. But this carpet's the kind of thing I like, a real beaut! Always wanted a wall-to-wall carpet with roses in the middle. Can't say I like Persian rugs much; design's too finicky. This is more in my line— roses the size of an elephant's foot, so's you don't have to squint to make out what they are! It cost us a cool hundred, or was it more, Bert?"

"Whyn't you keep the price-tag on?" grumbled her husband good-naturedly. Dolly continued, unruffled: "Our bedroom suite cost a packet, lovely bit o' work. I'll take you up to see it later. We got parkey flooring in all the rooms, too, no more of this cement for me. Cost a fortune, though, that did."

Throughout her discourse Dolly showed no trace of pretentiousness or conceit; hers was the simple pleasure of a

child showing off her toys to an admiring group of nursery
playmates. When she paused to regain her breath, Pierre
murmured: "Ah yes, I'm sure the other rooms are as
charmingly furnished as this one." She mistook his repressed
yawn for a wistful *moue* and became at once compassionate
over our own financial shortcomings. Covered with confusion
and self-reproach for having unwittingly drawn such comparisons in our respective situations, the big-hearted woman
hastened to assure us that she and Bert had endured a hard
struggle in the "early days". By all accounts they had come
close to starvation.

"My God! We had a time of it, didn't we, Bert love? I remember wondering if we'd *ever* have a proper bathroom,
much less a dining-room. Bert got this farm soon as we
married, you see, and we didn't have a bean to call our
own. All borrowed capital. And all the capital we did have
had to go into tractors and such. We built a little wattle-and-
daub place. Just two rooms. One where we slept and ate,
and the other where we cooked. The boy filled a tin tub with
water from the river when we wanted a bath. We didn't get
no fresh water; had to boil it all for drinking. An' those
blasted lamps and smoking candles, remember, Bert? Got
our own electric plant here now. The thatch wasn't too hot
either; it leaked like a mucking sieve whenever it rained. I
didn't start any babies, for which I blessed the saints, so I
stuck into farm work along with Bert. Used to get my glad
rags on about once every two months to shop in Salisbury.
Went in a truck that shook the guts out of me all the way,
and when we got there I'd spend an hour just looking in the
windows of all the posh shops, then make for the bazaars.
No fancy prices for this babe in those days, hey, Bert love?"

"Like Thoreau," I suggested, "you chose to be rich by
making your wants few."

"I beg yours, I didn't quite catch?"

An explanation was spared by the arrival of further guests. "Cooee!" cried a feminine voice, and a moment later the owner tripped into the room on four-inch heels, followed by a man who appeared to be resigned to melancholy. Dolly Goldman grunted to her feet and went forward.

"Why, Freda Harris, you damned snob! You haven't been over to see us for weeks! Anyway, you've chosen a good day, you can meet Pierre's wife. Carol meet Freda. That big hunk of a miserable male who's already at the radio is her husband, Mike. What you gonna drink? Come an' tell us all about everything!"

Mrs Harris patted her bright blond hair and smiled at me. Her plucked eyebrows gave her face an expression of mild astonishment which never varied, and the carmine of her nails was dimmed by the lustre of an immense ruby ring.

Had one seen Mrs Harris polishing tumblers at the bar of the Red Lion, indulging in broad jests and good-humoured gossip, one would not for a moment have considered her to be an impostor. Yet had one seen Mrs Harris polishing her gold-framed sun-glasses, reclining on a beach at Cannes, while an amorous but impoverished Italian nobleman murmured sweet somethings in her ear and discreetly examined her diamond bracelet, one would never have doubted the solidity of her opulence.

"I've been meaning to drop in for ever so long, my dear, but you know what it is. Been one mad rush since we got back from Cape Town. Drink? Aw, Bert, gimme a whisky!"

She sat down on the arm of my chair and swung her well-shaped legs, then turned to me and said: "How're you finding this little dump? When Mike first brought *me* out here as a blushing bride I damn nearly caught the first plane back to London!"

Across the room her husband raised his sad, spaniel eyes.

"What's all this about a blushing bride, honey?" he asked. "You got all the blushing part over by the time you were fifteen, if what I hear's true!"

"Aw, go on! I never had to blush. Dad kept pigs in Suffolk, so I knew all about it, anyway!"

This light-hearted domestic banter caused Dolly Goldman considerable amusement. "Oh, you two!" she gasped. "It does my poor soul good to hear you! Tell me, Freda, how was Cape Town? D'you have a nice holiday?"

"You bet we did," said Freda, scattering cigarette ash on the roses of the carpet. "We stayed at the Nelson and got a bellyful of the best food I've tasted for months, and drank enough whisky to float a battleship. Mike played snooker with his cronies and I ran riot in the dress shops, and the hat shops and the shoe shops. My, but they'd got some lovely clothes in, Doll!"

On the other side of the room Mr Goldman and Mr Harris sat tensely beside the wireless, oblivious to all but the voice of the commentator, who seemed to have taken possession of the programme for the entire morning. With a Frenchman's horror of cricket Pierre was forced to keep abreast of our feminine chatter, and his boredom betrayed itself by his eager but often irrelevant entries into the conversation, which he made with the conscious guilt of one who has not been giving the subject of the conversation his undivided attention.

The dress shops, shoe shops and milliners of Cape Town were being discussed in minute detail when Pierre said: "Ah yes, I believe the drives are beautiful . . . old oak trees, and the Huguenot houses." Freda looked at him with surprise and momentary suspicion. However, when she saw that his eyes were fixed in dreamy vacancy on the ceiling, she relaxed and lit another cigarette.

"Oh, it's a lovely place, no kidding!" she said. "Saw an art exhibition there, too."

Dolly squawked: "You never!"

"Yes, we did, too. There was a poster thing about it in the foyer of the Nelson. It was contemp'ry French art, and I said to Mike: 'Come on, Mike, let's go!' I said, 'even if it's only to look at the nudes.' "

Pierre regarded her with twinkling eyes. "*Were* there any nudes?" he asked.

"Well, I can't reelly say . . . I think there must've been, but they'd sort of disguised them the way they do in this contemp'ry art. I must say it was quite exciting—there were lots of peculiar people about. There was one girl, very arty—you know, thin and lah-di-dah—and she said she thought the pictures were a 'visual sensation'. I must say the colours hit you in the eye. Poor old Mike, though! He was so fed up with it all. Wouldn't even buy me a catalogue. You do feel a bit of a fool looking at a picture when you don't know what it's supposed to be. I mean to say, when you look at a picture you should *say* something about it. I tried to think of something clever to say, like visual sensation. All I could think of was 'optical illusion' but I expect it means the same thing."

## CHAPTER FIVE

THE Barnetts were the only farmers in the immediate neighbourhood whom I had not yet met, and Betty Harker had said that they were very well connected. With such people one must undoubtedly encourage friendship to that degree of intimacy which permits one to address them on an equal footing. Mrs Harker had also remarked upon Veronica Barnett's exquisite underwear, and on that point curiosity alone made the acquaintance of the Barnetts a necessity.

We had not been invited but we overcame this handicap by lending a purpose to our call. Among their accomplishments the Barnetts were reputed to breed Siamese cats. I had an urge to possess a Siamese kitten.

The Barnetts resided in a very large house designed by a notable architect. The classic façade, with its preponderance of chimneys and pedimented dormer windows reminiscent of Inigo Jones, was given the African touch with a facing of granite slabs and the incorporation of immense granite boulders on either side of the portico. The boulders were decorated in ochre with pseudo-Bushman paintings; the combination of classic colonnades with the art of the Bushman seemed a little strange.

Our arrival had already been noted and a shadow moved behind the opaque glass doors. They were thrown open and the substance of the shadow appeared in the form of a young woman, elegantly tall and slim. One is sometimes made aware, when seeing a new face, of either the flesh or the bone in the human structure. With Veronica Barnett it was the bone. Her features were sharp, the nose high-bridged, the cheeks excessively hollow, the teeth protrudent. The days of wearing braces on the teeth as a child must be over, for in the high-stepping models of today protruding teeth combined with hollow cheeks and arched eyebrows denote the quintessence of blue-blooded arrogance.

Mrs Barnett smiled faintly and said: "Oh, Constable de Choisy, isn't it?"

"Yes," said Pierre. "May I introduce my wife, Carol?"

"Your *wife*? Did you get married recently? What fun! I had no idea. Of course we don't indulge in the local grapevine. How do you do?"

"How do you do?" I said.

"I must say this is an unexpected pleasure. Are you on one of your—um, patrols, Constable?"

Pierre raised an eyebrow and smiled. "A patrol in my *own* car, *with* Carol and *out* of uniform? I'd be asking too much of the Force, though I'd find it very pleasant, certainly. No,

D

Carol is rather keen to have a Siamese kitten and we came to see if you had any going a-begging?"

Mrs Barnett turned to me with an expression of feigned astonishment. "Do you *really* want one? What fun! We don't charge for them, of course. I think it's perfectly ridiculous the way people *sell* things nowadays. . . ."

We followed her into the drawing-room and found there a plump young man reclining on the sofa with a copy of *Country Life*. Mrs Barnett introduced her husband, then excused herself and departed in search of the kittens.

Grahame Barnett had a smooth, pink face and a petulantly drooping mouth.

"You looked very comfortable when we came in," said Pierre. "Most farmers round here convey the impression that life is one long battle against the elements."

Grahame caressed a cheroot with his plump fingers and laughed. "Great Scott, no! If it were, I'd throw in the sponge and go on the stage, or something. Be too utterly grim. No, I generally have a good nap in the afternoon and ride out after tea to see what my young assistants are up to. I've got two fellows out from Home to chase the niggers along. So long as the work gets done, I see no reason to wear myself out over the details." He turned to me: "Won't you have a drink, Mrs er—I forget the name. A Martini? Pink gin?" He cupped his hands and roared: "*Boy!*"

A young African wearing a red, tasselled fez answered the summons with alacrity and was dispatched with the curt command: "Tray. Glasses. Ice. Quick."

Veronica came in with two Siamese kittens cradled in her arms. "I can't think where the others are," she said. "These two seraphic-eyed bundles are both toms. Rather fun!"

Their little chocolate paws dangled over their creamy tummies and their china-blue eyes roamed about the room till I bent over them, when they fixed their gaze on me in silent judgement. One of them yawned and averted his eyes so I chose the other.

"I'll shut him up in one of the bathrooms till you're ready to leave," said Veronica. This implied that she expected us to extend our visit, and her husband produced a box of Turkish cigarettes to confirm the implication.

When Veronica returned she fitted a cigarette into a long ivory holder before sinking into an armchair. She caught my eye and said: "It's rather fun, isn't it? My holder, I mean. I bought it in Dar-es-Salaam. I can't *bear* any other cigarettes than these. Mummy always smokes them and I picked up the habit from her when I was a débutante. Chain-smoking and late nights seem to go hand in hand, don't they? Like oysters and champagne. La, I have a craving to taste a fresh oyster again—what are you going to do about *that*, Grahame?" She turned to me. "I must say the restaurants in Salisbury are rather fifth-rate aren't they? I mean they never manage to serve wine at the right temperature, chilled or *chambré*. All the food seems to be tinned; and the Camembert is always as hard as Cheddar! Never mind, Grahame darling"—she pronounced it "dhulling"—"Do you find, as I do, Mrs de Choisy, or shall I call you Carol? Right, Carol. What was I saying? Oh, yes. Do you find that though one yearns for London and Paris, and perhaps even St Moritz, *unbearably*, one can get an absurd amount of fun out of these Colonial backwaters? I mean they are rather fun."

Grahame said: "Great Scott, yes! But some things out here really are too utterly grim. Tailors, for instance. Great Scott! It seems good tailors simply don't exist in this country. Do *all* the men here buy ready-made suits? Another thing I miss is the theatre. I mean, you really can't expect our Salisbury Repertory to do justice to the sort of things that are running at Wyndham's or the Lyric. Be too utterly grim. By and large Rhodesia has very little to offer except money, has it?"

The things that the Barnetts missed increased in number, and Pierre and I nodded or shook our heads in sympathy, while a variety of names for the new kitten ran through my mind. I worked alphabetically and decided that names beginning with "A" were unsuitable. On to the "Bs". "Baloo"? "Boswell"? "Bigglesworth"? "Baboushka"? "Baboushka. . . ."

It was Veronica's turn again, and I must have telepathised a "B" into her mind. "And the Bois de Boulogne," she said. "Do you remember, dhulling? That heavenly spring day...."

"Baboushka", I decided. Then, vaguely following the trend of the Barnetts' duologue, I held a silent one of my own. I was in London—perhaps even St Moritz: "*The first, fresh mouthful of a summer paw-paw. . . . La, I have a craving to taste a fresh paw-paw again—what are you going to do about that, Pierre? Do you find, as I do, Mrs Barnett, or shall I call you Veronica? Right, Veronica. What was I saying? Oh, yes. Do you find that though one yearns for the warmth and space of Africa, and perhaps even the mosquitoes,* unbearably—*one can get an absurd amount of fun out of these ski-resort backwaters? I mean they are rather fun. . . . Great Scott, yes! But some things here really are too utterly grim. Servants for instance. Great Scott! It seems servants simply don't exist in this country. Do all the women here have to do their own washing —or pay laundrymen? Another thing I miss here is the scent of frangipani at night. I mean, you really can't expect a débutante's dabs of 'My Sin' to do justice to the breath of a moonlit frangipani blossom. Be too utterly grim . . . and the Zambesi valley—do you remember, dhulling? That sweltering hot day?*"

Pierre had observed my expression, or lack of it, and leant towards Grahame. "Could we have a look at your seed beds?" he asked. "I'd like to show Carol what young tobacco plants look like."

"Rather! By all means. I was going to ride over on Nabob but we'll go in the jeep."

"Oh, dhulling, what fun!" said Veronica. "But—the jeep? It's so fearfully *jolting*. Couldn't we go in the Jaguar?"

"All the same to me. The Jag it is then." Grahame stirred a fat, somnolent spaniel with his toe. "Come on, Melody!" He had exchanged the tone of the nostalgic dilettante for the hearty joviality of the country squire, urging his guests to a brisk tramp over the fields. He lacked a shooting stick, but the wheezing Melody heaved herself up from the carpet and played her part faithfully by trotting out behind him.

Out in the yard I was conscious of Veronica's high heels tapping, Grahame's voice nasally droning, the old spaniel wheezing, and somewhere in the background another sound —the neighing of a horse.

The call of a horse is an unravelling of triumph and sadness. It has in it a compelling, primordial urgency. A high echo of manless, windswept places. It ends on a small, harsh throb that calls in desolate sorrow for an unremembered freedom.

"That's Nabob," said Grahame over his shoulder. "The boy brought him in after lunch and he wants to get out, impatient devil. Listen to him kicking the stable door. Do you ride? Jimmy Wright's organising a gymkhana at his place next week; why don't you come? Veronica and I will probably go in for a few events, if they're not too utterly grim and juvenile."

Veronica caught his eye. "I said I *may*, dhulling. You know how Rajah behaves in a crowd; he gets all excited and rears, or else he decides not to budge an inch, the beast!"

We purred up the farm road in the Jaguar, still discussing the gymkhana. Though she did not indulge in the local grape-vine, Veronica seemed well informed as to who were to be among the entrants, and on what points of equitation they would fail. She was, however, more concerned with the probability of what the spectators would be wearing.

"I *know* Mrs Ellis-Parker will arrive in that frightfully ancient straw pancake she calls her ex-Ascot hat, won't she, dhulling? And Freda Harris will squeeze herself into that electric blue thing. I suppose Betty will sway over us all in one of her enormous Mexican cartwheel hats. What fun!"

Mexican cartwheels or recalcitrant Rajahs, it was undoubtedly going to be fun and the prospect delighted me.

Grahame drew up at the side of the road. "We have to walk from here," he said. We were led down a steep gully and over the rise. Veronica had removed her shoes, murmuring: "What fun!" despite the fact that she tore her stockings at the outset. The tobacco seed beds were spread down the slope in orderly rows. Some were covered with taut sheets of muslin, some mulched with fine golden grass, and others, with plants already almost a foot high, rippled in waves of vigorous green. An African moved slowly down one of the beds with a pair of shears, bending low to clip the tops off the broad leaves. He was accompanied by a freckled, sunburnt youth in khaki, who turned shyly away when he saw us approaching.

"What on earth are they doing?" I asked.

"Oh, those are the first beds we sowed," said Grahame. "Most of the plants in them have got pretty big and they're cutting them back, as we haven't had enough rain to plant out yet. If you allow them to get too big in the seed beds they'll begin to flower before they've made enough leaf. Young Anthony's following Moses to see he only clips the outside leaves; if he cuts off the heart of the plant, it dies."

We walked between the rows, watching the soft silver spray that swung across the beds in a wide arc from the shining pipelines of the overhead irrigation. The sun burned hot on our backs and an emerald-spotted dove called mournfully down the scale from the *msasa* trees.

I asked to see the smallest seedlings, that were shaded with muslin, and Grahame unpegged and lifted one corner. I saw nothing. Then bending closer I discerned faint specks of green, each leaf barely larger than a pinhead.

"Do you have to do anything special to the beds before you sow?" asked Pierre.

"Great Scott, yes! They're treated with chemicals first, for eel-worm you know, and then a few weeks later we burn faggots of wood over them to discourage weeds. The seed's awfully fine—one level teaspoon of seed mixed with ash or water is sufficient for a bed of four feet by twenty-five yards. And a bed of that size planted out will do more than an acre."

Veronica patted back a yawn, and her husband suggested we had seen all there was to be seen. As I rose to go, I saw the tiny miracles of life stir under the gust of my breath, unaware that they were growing for man's delight—to be cured and shredded and rolled in thin white paper; to be blown away in rising tendrils of smoke at a crowded cocktail party; or, on the deck of a ship, to be tossed overboard, the paper uncurling and the last fragments of tobacco sinking in the hissing waves.

When we drove away with Baboushka we fully anticipated a display of feline resistance with spits, scratches and swear-words, or, at the very least, a frightened, puzzled kitten, mewing and clinging and losing his shaky balance in the unaccustomed confines of the car.

But a cat draws upon secret resources to assume a composure he may not feel. Unlike a dog, who expresses every mood with unashamed frankness, a cat can act. Baboushka was well aware of the futility of resistance, and was, moreover, perfectly capable of looking after his own interests. He cast himself in the part of an experienced old cat to whom a car ride was as customary as a saucer of milk, and his performance was convincing.

Ignoring our overtures of friendship, he climbed on to the back seat of the car and sat there bolt upright, regarding with aloof indifference the passing scenery, and steadying himself over the bumps with tautened leg muscles and extended claws. I turned to admire him, calling his new name in a high-pitched squeak, because he was a baby and it is the done thing to squeak at babies. Baboushka's eyes were coldly critical and the skin of his back shuddered with disapprobation.

When we arrived at our cottage, I carried the kitten carefully in my arms, fearful of Pilchard's reception. But Baboushka caught the dog scent with his delicate, retroussé nose and found the smell somewhat similar to that of a fat spaniel whom he despised. He ejected himself forcibly from my grasp and landed lightly on the floor before the astounded Pilchard, dismissing the puppy with a decisive but innately well-bred spit. Then he extended a hind leg and began to wash himself. Pilchard whined and cocked his head, appealing to me with his eyes and the tip of his tail. I smiled. He lost control and leapt forward, shrieking, yapping, laughing, and rolling the kitten over with his clumsy paws. Darting round him, snapping at the air, and in to the attack again, pouncing and withdrawing. Baboushka waited for the opportunity to retreat and, when it came, bounded up on to the window-sill. He sat there frisking his tail and looking icily over our heads. He brought back dim memories of an old lady I knew called Miss Knight, a teacher of mathematics with a bitter tongue. I saw her frozen blue eyes fixed on the ceiling and heard the familiar words which used to drop from her scarcely parted lips: "When you have *quite* finished your little game in the back row, perhaps we may continue."

\*     \*     \*

Approaching the Native Commissioner's residence, I saw that a flutter of women were already assembled on the lawn. Mrs Fanshawe, the N.C.'s wife, was giving a little tea-party. Earlier in the week she had paid me her first social call, with gentle apologies for not having done so sooner.

"The baby has been teething and *thoroughly* miserable, poor little mite, and nanny couldn't do a *thing* with him, so I've been kept at home just lately. . . ."

Sipping her tea—to say that she drank her tea would sound uncouth—she had told me that once every few months she thought it a good idea to encourage all the Dzokuti wives to forgather, *en famille*, so to speak. "You know, it's quite absurd but, in spite of the fact that we all live within a stone's throw of each other, we are inclined to go about our little daily chores and get out of touch with one another, and I do think it such a pity."

Her call had been brief, and when she departed I could neither recall the colour of her hair, eyes or complexion, but was left with an impression of a light straw hat, white court shoes, floral print, and the words "gracious", "charming" and "ladylike".

When I joined the chattering throng on the lawn, Mrs Fanshawe gave me a warm welcome. Everyone was fully occupied in persuading everyone else to sit down. Deck-chairs were shunted backwards and forwards with a most eager concern as to whether the sun would be too trying, the shade too cool, or the negligible breeze too gusty.

"Sit here, Miss Storm!" said Betty Harker. "Then you'll be able to see Mrs Fanshawe's lovely petunias!"

"Oh, but where will you sit, Mrs Harker?" said Belinda.

"Won't you sit here, Mrs Dutoit?" asked Mrs Fanshawe, and Mrs Dutoit replied that that was very nice and sat down.

"Where will you sit?" Jennifer asked of Brenda Fawcett,

and Brenda said: "Oh—after you, Jennifer, but I must sit with my back to the sun, the glare's too terrible."

Betty Harker bustled about embracing her Pekingese, which snuffled irritably beneath her chin. "Now, what about *you*, Mrs Fanshawe," she boomed. "You *must* sit in our midst so that we can all talk to you at once!" Disposing of her hostess in one of the chairs, she cast her bird-bright eyes about and discovered that Jennifer and I were still at large.

"Come along, you two! Carol, you sit here, and Jennifer there, and I'll sit here next to Mrs Fanshawe. And if you're *very* good, Porky-pie, you can stay on Mumsie's lap!"

With a little more discreet edging and shifting we were all comfortably settled and ready for our tea, which appeared with such exact timing that I suspected Mrs Fanshawe's staff of watching us, with trays poised, from the kitchen windows.

"Aha!" said Betty Harker, when the two white-uniformed Africans appeared. "I always expect a magnificent spread here, and I'm never disappointed!" She turned to me, "Of course, you know, Mrs Fanshawe is an excellent cook; now don't deny it, Mrs Fanshawe, you *know* you are! I shall allow myself another three hundred calories today."

Buxom, blithe Belinda leaned forward and clapped her hands, "Oh, goody, goody! Chocolate éclairs!"

"I scarcely dare touch anything," said Brenda Fawcett, with a disapproving glance at Belinda's exuberance. "I'm developing the most atrocious spare tyre."

"So am I," said Jennifer Burkitt, "but I'm going to inflate it just the same!"

"Oh, it's nothing, really. Just a few odds and ends," said Mrs Fanshawe.

Absorbed at first with the éclairs, petit fours, Swiss rolls, and fruit cake, talk was less than sporadic. But just when a bystander might have begun to wonder if this silent and ruminative party satisfied Mrs Fanshawe's concepts of "keeping in touch", fingers were daintily licked, crumbs flicked away, and everyone drew a breath and began to talk.

We discussed black spot on roses, and at what age babies should be put on to solids; remarked upon the sauciness of the girl on the telephone exchange; compared grievances against cook boys, and had an animated ten minutes on the necessary proximity of the male paw-paw tree to the female. There was some controversy over the washing of knitted garments to prevent shrinking or stretching, and an even more stimulating disputation on the best way of exterminating ants in the pantry. In argument we became slightly flushed or faintly chilly according to temperament.

Betty Harker revived the spirit of conviviality by introducing the subject of the forthcoming dance; but that inevitably led to mention of the newcomer, Oliver Lindsay, and animosity returned.

"Belle's met him; I haven't," said Irma Dutoit flatly. Both Betty Harker and Brenda Fawcett leant forward with expressions of resentful amazement, then recollected themselves and leant back with expressions of affable surprise. Belinda blushed.

"Oh, I've hardly really met him," she said defensively. "I was taking little Angy for a walk and a young man passed us in a jeep, and then he reversed back to ask if we wanted a lift, and introduced himself as Oliver Lindsay. He seemed rather jolly."

"Jolly?" said Brenda sweetly, "I should hardly describe him as *jolly*. It's the sort of term one usually bestows on little, round-faced men, don't you think? And he's really rather dynamic!"

Betty Harker said: "I found him very——" she broke off with a little shrug and smiled into her tea-cup, as though dwelling on some intimate memory she would rather not divulge. Mrs Fanshawe was determined to dispel the constraint.

"I've found an absolute *treasure* of a cook boy," she said brightly. "I really feel guilty when I think what he would probably earn in England. I mean if you had a cook in England who could make such delicious soup and foamy omelettes he'd cost you the earth, and the only difference really would be his colour, though possibly he'd wash himself more often and keep his kitchen cleaner than my old Murapatse does!"

"I haven't found a cook at all," said Irma tartly. "They're none of them worth more than a few shillings in my opinion."

Mrs Fanshawe smilingly offered Irma another cup of tea, then said: "We English are really rather a peculiar race. Doesn't it strike you as being a little ironical that in England the cry to show the 'Black Man' justice and give him his rights is so very loud, and out here it is always those recently emigrated *from* England who are the first to express intolerance at his stupidity, and at the same time to show fear that he may eventually oust us from the country." Mrs Dutoit could think of no satisfactory reply. Belinda bit into an éclair and said: "Well I don't understand the natives, but I do understand that they need understanding."

Conversation lagged a little, and late afternoon shadows crept along the lawn. The stillness was suddenly shattered. Mrs Fanshawe's cook appeared from the kitchen premises shouting, leaping and grimacing. He clutched a wooden meat mallet. He was joined by the house-boy who brandished a floor-mop. A garden boy emerged from the tool shed with a long-handled, three-pronged cultivator.

"*Gonzo! Gonzo!*" yelled the cook.

"*Nyama!*" chorused the other two.

"It's the Mau Mau all over again," breathed Belinda, pressing her éclair till the cream oozed over her unconscious fingers.

"It's quite all right," said Mrs Fanshawe. "There seem to be nests of the horrid things all over the garden. I'd rather they didn't choose this moment to exterminate them but when they discover them they become absolutely hysterical. They do love them so!"

"Rats, you know," said Jennifer to the mystified Belinda. "They eat them."

"Oh!"

The three Africans advanced upon a thicket of bamboo that grew beyond the kitchen door. They dived into it with a sudden frenzied haste and struck wildly about them, uttering shrill cries of delight, oblivious of the glancing blows their own heads frequently received in the skirmish.

Several baby rats escaped between their legs and scampered over the lawn. Betty Harker's Pekingese struggled from her lap and flew after them shrieking, like a streak of dirty cotton wool. The houseboy was shaken with a fit of the giggles and ran in aimless circles, swinging a bunch of little grey corpses by their tails. The cook boy thudded across the lawn on Porky's heels, and the garden boy continued to probe the bamboos, beating methodically, pocketing each freshly killed rat with a contented grunt.

Mrs Fanshawe was forced to make herself heard with a voice of indecorous strength before she succeeded in disbanding her staff.

"It's rather interesting," she said, regaining her sangfroid when they had all trudged sheepishly back to their duty, "though whether it's true or not I don't know, but Harold tells me that there's a type of pouched rat eaten only by married people—Africans I mean—and a sort of reddish variety eaten only by the piccanins."

"Disgusting, filthy creatures!" said Irma Dutoit. She may have been referring to the rats for she shuddered convulsively. I thought it would be uncharitable to draw her attention to a very baby rat which I distinguished beneath a petunia plant, unscathed, cleaning its face.

When I returned to our cottage, Pierre was still absent on a motor-bike patrol. A soft rain began to fall, sliding with a sigh down the roof and dropping silently on glistening leaves. I turned on the wireless and listened to the atmospherics interspersed with a faint rendering of the "Blue Tango". But in the sputtering pops and plaintive notes I too often thought I heard the distant hum of a returning motor-bike. Pilchard and Baboushka followed me disconsolately outside.

The drizzle drifted away in the mournful arms of a night mist. Stars careered about the sky, glowing a moment, mockingly, then vanishing, racing one another to the next opening in the blanket of cloud.

Baboushka and Pilchard and I were suddenly dazzled by the lights of an approaching vehicle which swished through the mud and turned into our drive. A person of some size stepped out and a vaguely familiar voice called: "Good evening to you!" It was Oliver Lindsay.

"I was passing through when it occurred to me that the charming Mr and Mrs de Choisy might offer me a quick drink and some pleasant conversation! Was that very forward of me?" He loomed up in the shadows, and though it was too dark to discern his features I felt his eyebrows were being exercised.

"No, not very. I'm sure Pierre would have been delighted. Unfortunately he's out on a patrol, but he should be back at any moment. Come in."

"He's away? Ah! How very fortunate for me! 'Moon of my desire that knows no wane . . . a flask of wine—and *thou*! What boots it to repeat, how time is slipping underneath our feet.' Etcetera, etcetera!''

As he followed me to the veranda I caught a glimpse of the moon, wet-ringed and lemon-coloured, floating hazily above us. If anything happened to Pierre, the moon would simply be a blotch in the sky.

Oliver accepted a glass of sherry and sat with his long legs stretched out before him. "I've just had the most unnerving experience" he said, offering me a cigarette. "I very nearly lost my reputation which I fight so valiantly to retain. It all began when I called in at the Harkers' store the other evening for supplies, and discovered that the jeep had a flat tyre and no spare wheel. I had to telephone Jimmy with an S.O.S. to come and fetch me, and the Harkers pressed me to wait in their lounge. They had an engagement and left me to my own devices while they dressed for it. I was examining some photographs of quite repugnant-looking school girls on the mantelpiece when Betty Harker swept into the room. She said: 'Basil's gone to put petrol in the car and my zip has stuck. Would you be a dear and undo it for me?' And she turned and presented me with a very imperious and rather naked back. What, under those circumstances, does one do? One can hardly tell the woman that her husband may come in at any moment and be righteously indignant to find a comparative stranger fumbling with the fastening of his wife's dress. It would be so naïve. I grabbed the catch of the zip and yanked it loose. But in my haste I caught it again on the material of the dress. Oh, the cursed contumacy of inanimate objects! Horribly embarrassing! She kept screwing her head back to look at me while I tussled with the thing, and had I not been sober I would have sworn that her look was 'fraught with meaning', to use the popular expression. At all events my

relief was definitely greater than hers when the zip finally
released itself. Dear me, what with designing old dowagers
and reasonably youthful spinsters and witty young matrons
from the Bahamas, life is never dull! I'm always at my
happiest as a macaroni."

"A macaroni?"

"A macaroni. Lothario, beau, blade, cavalier."

"I see. And by reasonably youthful spinsters I take it you
mean Miss Storm?" I asked.

"Storm! That's it. Storm in a teacup. I couldn't for the
life of me remember her name. Yes, she seemed remarkably
*pure*. Sort of round-eyed and be-dewed I mean. She was
taking that dreadful little Dutoit child for a walk, and
refused my offer of a lift, which I thought very unkind of her.
I was only trying to inject a little romance into her life. I
mean, she knew that I knew that she was going for a walk.
Perhaps she's been told never to accept a lift from a Young
Man in a Car. So if I'm going to abduct her I shall have to
think up some other way."

Oliver's facetious banter lifted my depression. He flitted
from one topic to another and alighted on the gymkhana.

"Are you entering?" I asked him.

"Entering? My dear girl, I've been so busy erecting banks
and fences and digging water-jumps and ditches, and level-
ling and marking our and racking my brain for original
obstacles, that I doubt if I shall have the strength to climb
on a horse when the great day comes. Jimmy has had his
entire farm seething with activity over this gymkhana of his
for days. Seriously though, it should be rather good. He's
lending me a damn fine polo pony for it. You positively must
come, as I shall gallop past you like a knight in a tourna-
ment, and you must be ready to throw me a favour—a piece
of your sleeve is the correct thing, I believe. But you must be
fair and aim it well. So humiliating if I failed to catch it!"

"What about the fair Belinda?"

"Ah. I was coming to that! Having caught your token and pressed it fervently to my lips—quite a thing that, for a knight in armour; one has to lift the visor you know—I shall then tuck it through my chain mail next to my hanky with a tragic sigh, acknowledging the prior claim of your liege lord, Sir Pierre. In my frustrated passion I shall grab the fair Belinda—at full gallop mind, no mean feat, that—and hoist her up behind the saddle. Then we disappear into the setting sun with her terrified screams fading behind us. I'm all for Romance. Do I hear the put-put of a returning motor-bike?"

The faint sound grew louder and Pilchard's eyes met mine in confirmation. Pierre was back at last. Oliver's eyebrows quivered.

"Next time he goes out on patrol let me know well in advance, will you? I haven't made half as much progress this evening as I had hoped to. When I dropped in on Mrs Fawcett recently I read her fortune in the palm of her hand . . . there was a little interplay of fingers. Quite delightful!"

He rose to go when Pierre came in, but was persuaded to remain for another drink.

"Oliver is going to abduct Miss Storm at the gymkhana," I told Pierre, "but by all reports I think it far more likely that Mrs Harker and Mrs Fawcett will make a concentrated rush to abduct Oliver!"

"That," said Oliver, holding his sherry up to the light, "is what I am determined to avoid. Why am I always thwarted in my efforts to seduce maidens, and forced instead to shield myself from the advances of women who should know better?"

"Why, indeed?" muttered Pierre.

## CHAPTER SIX

"TO the Gymkhana" had been painted in shaky letters, not yet dry, on a board erected at the junction of Jimmy Wright's farm track and the main road.

Billy Burkitt swung the police Land-Rover up the bumpy track, humming "D'ye ken John Peel?" Pierre was to take part in the gymkhana with the old police horse, and Billy, Jennifer and I were to be among the cheering spectators. Jennifer and I had consequently selected our gayest dresses to wear, with high heels, shady hats and sun-glasses.

Dick Turpin had been carefully groomed for his public appearance and, led by an African constable, had departed for Jimmy's farm in the cool of the early morning.

Upon our arrival Jennifer and I sought out our own little circle of friends from Dzokuti. The bulk of the throng was made up by farmers and their families from farther afield. Though in reality our Dzokuti associates clung together in a body, they yet endeavoured to appear casually independent of one another. They also seemed to be holding a contest to see who could acknowledge the greatest number of acquaintances in the general crowd. Some of their nods and smiles were received with such blank stares that one suspected a feigned acquaintanceship. A little mild cheating was apparently permissible.

Belinda Storm was there, twirling restlessly, laughing at every sally, wearing a gauzy picture hat and stiffened petticoats.

"Someone's lent dear little Angela a pony to ride," she told me, squeezing her eyes with a smile, "and Irma and John have taken her off to the paddock so that she and the pony can make friends!"

The Goldmans were there, exchanging pleasantries with Mike and Freda Harris. Freda was wearing, as Veronica Barnett had prophesied, a straining dress of electric blue.

The Native Commissioner, Mr Fanshawe, moved about the assemblage, discussing the weather and the prospects of the day, or exchanging a few kind words among his subordinates. Skilfully blending reserve with cordiality, so that when he had passed on they turned to each other with gratified faces and murmured that he was not such a bad old stick after all. Mr Fanshawe was a portly man in his early sixties, though with his soft, plump-moulded face and fading brown hair he might have been mistaken for a man ten years younger. He sprouted a thin, brittle moustache, wore spectacles, and loved such phrases as "the point before the House is . . ." and "without fear of contradiction I may say . . .". Should one of his staff attempt an excuse for some oversight or blunder, he would say: "Don't beggar the issue, my good man! Don't beggar the issue."

He showed the fussy pedantry of a man more inclined to perfect a detail than to visualise the outcome of larger issues.

It was rumoured that he had spent the earlier part of his life as an accountant.

Michael Fawcett stood a little apart, smoking in a pre-occupied silence.

"Is Brenda not here?" I asked him.

"Hmm? Oh, Brenda, yes, yes, she's here. Mrs Ellis-Parker offered one of her knock-kneed hacks to Brenda. I fear the whole episode might well prove to be disastrous. This morning certainly didn't augur well. Brenda hasn't worn her jodhpurs for rather a long time and donning them for the great event was such a struggle that she's been somewhat out of sorts, as it were, ever since. As my advice to let well alone has been ignored, I wash my hands of the whole affair. I believe she's 'trying out his paces' or some such nonsense at the moment."

We were joined by Derek Vaughn. "As Pierre does not appear to be with us, I conclude that he has succumbed to the spell of exhibitionism and is preparing Dick Turpin to surpass himself, thereby threatening us all with hideous embarrassment," he drawled at me, his hands deep in the pockets of his baggy flannels.

"Why," said Jennifer, "should Dick Turpin and Pierre cause you such hideous embarrassment?"

"Why, my dear Jennifer, for the simple reason that their performance will undoubtedly be lamentable, and instead of merging with the muttering crowd I must hold up my head in loyalty, acknowledging a friendship which, in the event of Pierre's disgrace, I should far rather did not exist! And you, my dear Michael! How could you condone your wife's abominable lapse into this equestrian hysteria which seems to have assailed so many gathered here today? I pray heaven she will comport herself with some dignity."

Michael threw away the butt of his cigarette and his face relaxed into a smile.

"You seem to have a deep distaste for horses, Derek. Between ourselves, so have I, but I daren't admit as much to Brenda or I shall be for ever branded a coward and she may even doubt the authenticity of my British ancestors."

"A horse," said Derek, teetering back and forth on his heels and gazing at the sky with disdain, "is a four-legged, urinating abomination." Michael laughed nervously, "Yes, er, yes, quite. Oh lord, here comes Brenda! I wonder what's gone wrong now?" She advanced with compressed lips and Jennifer and I thought it wise to withdraw.

This enabled us to witness the arrival of the Harkers which we should otherwise have missed. Their large car swept up with Betty at the wheel. She stepped out, adjusted the angle of her Mexican cartwheel hat, and bestowed a vague but gracious smile in the direction of the company. Her husband had already scuttled to the back of the car and was unlocking the boot.

"The field-glasses, Basil. And the rug, do fold it nicely, I will not have you dragging it all over the dirt. And bring my change of shoes, the grass looks a little damp. You may as well bring the tea flask at the same time, and my coat. Have you got the parasol? Now come along, dear, don't fuss! Just find a nice place where you can park and keep an eye on everything, I must go and greet Daphne Fanshawe." With these words she sailed away, while Mr Harker submissively folded the rug and coat, took up the flask and dropped the shoes, clung to the handle of the parasol with one frantically hooked finger and pottered off across the grass for several hesitant steps before discovering the absence of the field-glasses.

"Poor man, he reminds me of Mole in *Wind in the Willows*," said Jennifer. "Let's go to the paddock and see how Billy and Pierre are doing."

The paddock was a small field behind Jimmy Wright's stables, and presented a lively scene of preparation, and in many cases of opposing wills between horse and prospective rider. Pierre and Billy were using their combined efforts to tighten Dick Turpin's girths, while he defied their strength with every fibre of his swelling abdomen.

"Old bastard's trying to give out he's pregnant!" said Billy in disgust. At a short distance from them stood Veronica Barnett, tapping her calf with a silver-headed cane. She raised an eyebrow at Billy's unfortunate remark and turned her back.

In general turn-out the local riders tended to lay emphasis on comfort rather than correctness of attire. A great number of them wore khaki trousers or jeans and open-necked shirts. Some wore black riding-caps, some pith helmets, and others were bare-headed. The Barnetts, however, were beyond reproach. With shining boots and well-fitting breeches, exquisitely cut coats, faultless white stocks, well-brushed bowlers, hog-skin gloves, and, in the case of Grahame, a fresh white carnation in his buttonhole, they kept themselves aloof, and directed their African groom, Amos, in his final attentions to Rajah and Nabob.

Nabob was a good-looking dark bay of about sixteen hands. He held his head up proudly and gazed about him with soft, inquiring eyes.

"Morning!" said Grahame, on seeing us. "Looking rather lovely, isn't he? Seems hardly fair to let him compete with those other mules—too utterly grim. However, one must patronise these local shows, and he'll probably enjoy himself, the old plebeian!"

Veronica stepped over, still tapping her calf with the cane. "Do come and see if Rajah's all right, dhulling! Amos gets him so fidgety and I'm *sure* the curb's too loose, and my stirrups seem uneven and if I do them I'll get my gloves dirty.

Oh, hello, Carol! Would you be a dear and hold this while I powder my nose?"

I held her cane while she took a powder compact from her pocket and examined her face in the bright light. She dusted her nose with a puff, then snapped the case shut and looked about.

"I do detest these little gymkhanas!" she exclaimed. "They're always treated like funfairs where everyone goes about sucking oranges and eating ice-creams. No one else here seems to have the faintest notion of what a gymkhana implies. Though I believe the adult jumping is to be conducted according to B.S.J.A. rules. I suppose *someone* has checked the plan of the course, and the measurements and everything. Of course Rajah will be in a perfect *state* by the time that wretched Amos has finished with him! Not much fun, really."

I thought that Rajah, a bright chestnut with a pronounced ewe neck, looked particularly mild and unconcerned, but hesitated to say so for I felt she would misconstrue my meaning and regard any such reassurance as a reflection on her own lack of composure.

Leaving the Barnetts to vent their pent-up emotions on the quailing groom, I was drawn to another corner of the paddock where signs of violent dissension were taking place between Angela Dutoit and her parents. As I approached I heard Angela saying: "Oh, come *on*, you silly, fat thing, you! *Walk*, can't you?" She addressed a rotund Shetland pony astride which she sat.

"Speak to him nicely, dear; you'll make him nervous!" said Irma Dutoit. John said: "Ag, no man, she must show him who's master. Hit him, Angy, hit him an' he'll do what you want." The Shetland remained where he was with sturdy obstinacy, but at length, with Angela thumping his barrel-like frame with her heels, rocking to and fro in the saddle, and spasmodically jerking the reins, and her father administering resounding smacks on his fat rump, he lifted his sleepy, long-lashed eyes and moved forward two paces. Angela instantly abandoned the reins altogether to wave both arms in the air, yelling with jubilation. Mr Dutoit cried: "See! You gotta make him know who's boss! What did I tell you?" But it was a Pyrrhic victory, for the pony's aim had been a succulent clump of grass. No amount of friendly coaxing on the part of Mrs Dutoit, or masterful handling on the part of her husband, would induce him to move another step. He was, moreover, impervious to the piercing cries and frenzied performance of the child who bestrode him. Mr Dutoit caught my eye and said: "He's just a slug, that's all. Just a slug."

"Slug! Slug!" shrieked little Angela. The pony tore up a mouthful of grass and rippled a fly off his withers.

"Come and see the Bahamas, they're far more entertaining!" drawled a soft voice behind me. I turned to find Derek, with an impish smile, indicating a couple at the far end of the paddock.

"Apparently the inner seam of her jodhpurs split in her first efforts to mount and Michael had to hustle off to the car with her to help repair the damage with a needle and thread she had thoughtfully provided. She is now about to make a second attempt and we mustn't miss the spectacle!" He hurried me across with unseemly haste and we were in time to see Brenda, her feet supported by Michael's hands, edging herself up on a bony grey mare. Brenda waited till the saddle lay safely beneath her middle before slowly bringing her right leg up and swinging it over, rigidly extended. Her actions, though not elegant or orthodox, ensured the minimum strain on the seams of her jodhpurs, and once she had righted herself and collected the reins she assumed the look of a horse-woman who is both resolute and spirited.

Among those already mounted and intent upon exercising their horses at the top end of the paddock I perceived Oliver Lindsay. He trotted his lively polo pony alongside the fence, turned and came back at a slow canter, at which pace he executed a figure of eight, then came towards us on a loose rein, smiling and flicking imaginary dust from his coat-sleeve. On seeing Derek, his smile broadened.

"What? Not entering?" he cried in unconvincing distress. "I had hoped we would be pitting the strength of our steeds to win the fair Belinda!"

"No," said Derek, "I have not the slightest desire to sub-jugate the self-respect of the biped. And if the strapping young lady who is wearing what appears to be a cartridge-paper petticoat beneath her skirt is the fair Belinda I would prefer to conserve my strength for a more deserving candi-date."

The first event of the day was the jumping competition. Pierre, Oliver Lindsay, Brenda Fawcett and Grahame and Veronica Barnett were entering, together with a considerable number of others with whom we are not concerned.

To discuss the plan of the course, and the improvisation employed in the construction of the obstacles; to describe the manner in which Mr Fanshawe, who was judge, walked the course accompanied by Jimmy Wright, who was ring steward, measuring heights and spreads with the conscious air of one who wishes to appear unconscious; to attempt to portray the indifference, eagerness or apprehension reflected on the faces of the entrants as they inspected the course themselves—all this would involve me in a wealth of unnecessary detail. Suffice to say that there were in all seven fences: parallel bars; triple bars; brush; reversed oxer; gate; single rail; and a twelve-foot water-jump.

Following upon the hush caused by the first announce-ment, Mr Fanshawe put on his spectacles, took up a sheet of paper, and clearing his throat into the megaphone, which produced such an extraordinary sound that the more frivolous spectators were still giggling some twenty minutes later, he called for the first competitor and the gymkhana had begun.

After several riders had completed the course, some with a clear round executed with poise and competence, and others showing a regrettable lack of balance and control, Mrs V. Barnett made her entry into the arena. It was evident that Rajah maintained a calmness which Veronica did not possess. Her face was flushed and strained, and her seat uneasy. She seemed unable to decide upon a suitable length of rein, allowing Rajah sufficient slack to ease his jaw muscles, then drawing the reins in again with a bewildering violence that made him toss his head and lay back his ears—the only means by which the meek-natured horse could express his resentment. The starting bell was rung with encouraging vigour, but Veronica was as yet unsatisfied with herself and her mount. They continued to move back and forth in an aimless manner, Rajah becoming increasingly confused and Veronica more flustered. She put up a hand to adjust her bowler and in doing so released her grip on her silver-headed cane which fell to the ground.

"Oh, please, someone!" she called. But sixty seconds had elapsed since the clangor of the starting bell and Mrs V. Barnett was, not without protest, eliminated.

Dick Turpin came next in order, ridden by Pierre. Though Pierre looked exceedingly handsome in uniform, Dick Turpin could not disguise the fact that he was advancing in years and found it difficult to cut a dash. He lacked the speed and grace of former entrants and moved in a disunited and clumsy manner. In short, he lumbered. But despite the ungainly effect he cleared the fences, even the water, with a certain elderly dignity which won him considerable applause. Before the take-off he would check in his stride, eye the approaching obstacle with mistrust, then heave himself over with ponderous resignation. Pierre, I thought, would have been more suitably mounted on a fiery charger, or alternatively Dick Turpin should have carried some portly Jorrocks. But I was, in Brenda's words, a newly wed, and perhaps the sight of Pierre exposing himself to the ribaldry of his less charitable friends had made me unduly sensitive.

The next competitor, Brenda Fawcett, entered at a canter with a confident smile. The bony grey mare, which had been given the name of Hebe, swung off for the first fence with the excited haste of a horse who knows very well what a fence is made for, fully approves of the idea, and is excessively eager to display its ability. Brenda rose in her saddle and was heard to gasp: "Wait! Wait, they're torn again!" As her frantic appeal to the impatient Hebe was conveyed by no other means than a further verbal entreaty to "Wait! Wait!" one cannot take exception to Hebe's disobedience. The grey mare thundered on heedlessly, and Brenda clutched at her jodhpurs with one hand and grasped the pommel of the saddle with the other. Though any co-ordination between horse and rider which might have existed had now ceased entirely, Hebe nevertheless tucked up her forelegs and sprang blithely over the brush fence. Brenda was not unnaturally dislodged at the height of Hebe's ascent, but to give her credit she did not prolong our anxiety by moaning, or going into a swoon. She sat up hurriedly, and her face was more expressive of annoyance than pain. "Michael," she cried, "bring some safety pins, and for heaven's sake hurry!" With a dispirited air and dangling reins Hebe wandered over to the water jump to quench her thirst.

From Oliver Lindsay we anticipated a more accomplished performance, and on seeing the easy assurance with which he entered the arena it seemed that our expectations were to be gratified. Though the narrow-chested little polo pony he rode could well have made him appear heavy, Oliver displayed a suppleness that produced instead a feeling of pleasant harmony between horse and rider.

But the pony was hot, excitable and contrary. He refused the brush and had to be driven at it. He ran out at the single rail. Oliver's jaw became more pronounced, his seat less supple, his hand less sympathetic. The pony yielded and they swept over the triple bars, cleared the reversed oxer, hurtled over the gate . . . and landed in the water with a tremendous splash. That is to say, Oliver landed in the water. The pony had come to a halt on the brink with an abruptness that Oliver would not tolerate and we were impressed with his determination to clear the water alone, in brave defiance of the unwilling pony. I think it occurred to most of us that during those breath-held moments when he was submerged the memory of his own active part in supervising the construction of the water jump must have greatly exacerbated his already overtaxed temper, and been largely responsible for his angry refusal to make a second attempt at the obstacle.

Mr G. Barnett was announced, and cantered into the ring. Nabob moved with a lovely, rhythmic grace, alert yet relaxed. Of Grahame one could not say the same. Throughout his performance, though compelled to acknowledge his remarkable ability to remain mounted, we were dismayed to see such a willing horse persistently restricted in his efforts.

On approaching a fence Grahame would pivot up to a standing position on his stirrup-irons, knees held rigid, and maintain his balance by clinging to the reins with such desperation that his elbows projected like wings behind him. Despite the resulting lack of impulsion and freedom, Nabob never failed to soar over the obstacle, his upward movement throwing Grahame clear of the saddle so that he seemed suspended in the air like some predatory spider. Then the descent, the heavy thud back on to the saddle and the wild embrace of Nabob's glossy neck. That admirable horse would have executed several strides before Grahame could regain his customary seat, by which time the next jump was too near for him to exercise any show of control, and the whole un-happy set of motions would be repeated.

Over the water Grahame adopted a different position. He did not stand up but remained in the saddle, leaning far back with legs outstretched, exerting all his strength on the reins as though urging Nabob to desist from attempting the spread. In this peculiar attitude he was carried over without so much as wetting one of his feet, though he did lose his bowler at the outset. It landed on the water with a modest plop and bobbed and slid in the trough of the wave it had occasioned, as if, like some suave Fred Astaire, it glided with an animate deliberation, practising steps in a mocking dance of its own devising.

Grahame accepted the ovation awarded him with magnifi-cent aplomb, but Nabob threw up his head and rolled his velvety eyes with delight. The old plebeian!

There followed a tedious event, announced as "The Best Child's Pony Including Condition of Saddlery and General Turn-out". This entailed an arduously minute examination of each entrant, delayed at the start because the best children were too busy comparing tails and brow-bands and oiled hooves to acknowledge the presence of the judge. To draw favourable comparisons between their ponies and those of their rivals so engrossed the young competitors that the judge's final decision went by unheeded.

We were diverted by a lively "Mounted Musical Chairs". The music was provided by three young Africans who squatted over crude drums of their own making, beating them with a hypnotic fervency surpassing all the night-club percussion players that have ever sent their audience into a paralytic-faced, saxophone-pierced coma, and displaying the greater virtuosity, perhaps, because they claimed a closer affinity, though it were the merest shade, to the primitive than could the professional jazz band.

Lunch was served on trestle tables, set out in the shade of a roughly erected shelter. Among the women who had volunteered to do the catering, and now bustled solemnly up and down, arranging salads and paper napkins, we found Freda Harris briskly distributing cardboard plates, flashing a smile and a cheery "You're welcome!" to the few who thought to thank her.

We surged forward, a great many among us with ill-concealed haste. Indeed, I overheard one stout matron declare to her neighbour: "Well, of course, Liza, I do love watching the kiddies on their ponies, and the jumping was ever so exciting, wasn't it? But I must confess, my dear, I've been looking forward to the buffet"—she pronounced it "buffy"—"all the morning. I had a very light breakfast specially—just tea and a little toast and marmalade. . . . Such a lovely spread! But let me warn you, my dear"—her voice dropped to a whisper—"the sausage rolls will be indigestible, quite indigestible. Mrs Monksfoote made them. I know, because her cook boy told my cook boy and he told me. Her pastry is always so *heavy*! She really has no idea. . . ."

I glimpsed Belinda hurrying eagerly to the tables and being effectively forestalled by Oliver Lindsay who seemed bent on renewing their acquaintance.

"Oh, you're quite dry!" said Belinda.

"Oh, yes. I brought a change of things with me, I'd have changed, anyway, you know; one gets so horribly sticky riding in this weather. Though I must say my little immersion refreshed me no end. Most unpredictable creatures, horses. Of course, I suppose that tiny element of risk in riding is half the attraction; for me it is anyway. Do you ride yourself, Miss—er—Storm?"

"Oh no! Oh, Mr Lindsay, I'd be terrified! I'd fall off, I know I'd fall off!"

"Nonsense, I'm sure you ride very well. My name's Oliver, by the way."

"Oh? Oh, mine's Belinda. My sister calls me Belle. . . ."

Belinda gazed at Oliver with parted lips. But though his attentive manner brought a response composed in turn of gushing warmth and fluttering withdrawals, Mr Lindsay, in white breeches and black riding boots, had not yet so entirely absorbed her that the thoughts uppermost in her mind could be effaced. From time to time her eyes roved to the trestle tables and, while listening enthralled to an account of a narrow escape from disaster on a bolting horse, she contrived to draw him step by step nearer to her goal.

Brenda appeared. She had exchanged the guise of the resolute horsewoman for one of appealing defencelessness, and intercepted Oliver with a shy smile.

"Isn't the crush appalling? I simply can't face the idea of pushing through all these people for anything. Could you be a dear, Mr Lindsay, and just put a little something on a plate for me? I'm sure you'll get to the tables without any difficulty; you're head and shoulders above everyone else, with the possible exception of dear Betty Harker! Just a little salad and a few slices of tongue and ham, and a little of that brawn if you can manage it. Thank you *so* much, sweet of you. I see Belinda is already helping herself, so perhaps she'll be able to manage without you? I'll be waiting here." She turned and saw me.

"Pierre looking after you? It always pays to play the helpless female, doesn't it? Isn't Belinda a perfect scream with roses trailing all over her hat? Quite absurd! I notice she lost no time in making headway with Oliver. I rather think I may do the poor man a service by rescuing him. He is rather a pet, isn't he? I do think your Pierre looks awfully continental and dashing in uniform . . . makes such a difference. . . . I remember a devastating young Frenchman in the Bahamas, Maurice something or other. He always used to call me his '*chère innocente*' in a tone that implied anything but innocence. So amusing! Oh, you *were* quick! What a delightful lunch you've chosen for me, Oliver! I can't imagine where Michael is; he'll just have to fend for himself."

Pierre reached us with two plates held gingerly aloft.

"Hullo, Brenda," he said. "Recovered from your spill?"

"Oh yes! It was all so absurd. I mean, there was I with a gaping seam down one leg, transfixed with horror, and that wretched little horse racing along like an express train, *determined* to jump whether I wished it or no! *I* was in the most awful predicament and had no option but to vacate the saddle as gracefully as possible. Oh, here's Belinda. Gracious, what a healthy appetite! Will you get through all that alone, Belinda? I've been admiring your hat all the morning . . . those lovely roses! It doesn't shelter you from the sun though, does it? Your neck is scarlet!"

Betty Harker had seen Oliver. She pressed through the gathering. Unaware of the bitter comments she provoked as she tipped hard-won sausage rolls and pickles to the floor with her hips and elbows, and undaunted by the shameless behaviour of others who showed reluctance to make way for her, she arrived triumphant with her own lunch intact.

"Hallo! How are you, Brenda? A little tender? You did fall quite heavily, didn't you! What? You slipped off deliberately? Of course, I see. How clever of you, my dear! Hallo, Belinda. Why, child, you're dreadfully sunburnt! Isn't she, Oliver? Your nose is quite crimson. I should advise you to stay in the car for the rest of the afternoon, or you'll find it very painful tomorrow." She paused to bite a cold sausage and turned to Oliver.

"You did *so* well. I must own I was most disappointed in the Barnetts. Though I can't claim any great knowledge of riding, there did seem to be something a little wrong with Grahame's style. But perhaps he was using the Hunting Seat. Of course, Veronica is an *excellent* rider. Such a shame she was eliminated! I simply couldn't help admiring the way *you* handled that little brute of a pony, Oliver. He was obviously quite out of training and needed a very firm hand. Of course I knew you had the strength to manage him, but riding isn't entirely a matter of strength, is it? I mean the way you got him to go over all those jumps was superb. I very nearly wept when he threw you at the water jump, the little beast! You weren't hurt, were you? But of course you'd never admit it if you were; you're the sort of man who wouldn't complain over a thing like that. I do admire courage. My goodness, what a struggle it is to keep one's plate with all these people shoving one! I hope you don't object to my being continually crushed against you like this, Oliver? I'm being so buffeted on one side that it's awfully comforting to find your solid bulk on the other!"

"Well, don't push him *too* hard, dear," said Brenda; "remember I'm on the other side and I haven't sufficient strength to compete with yours!"

Belinda had been too intent upon her lunch to regard the beleaguering of Oliver with concern, until she looked up and, finding him harried with importune praise, firmly asserted her own claims.

"Oh, Mrs Harker," she cried, "you jogged Mr Lind . . ., Oliver's elbow and now he's got mustard on his lovely white breeches! Can I lend you my hanky, Oliver?"

Edging through the crowd once more, in the hopes of

E

finding a cup of coffee, Pierre and I found ourselves behind the Barnetts, who brooded on the morning's activities.

"But, darling, it was so utterly grim! What on earth put you off? Great Scott! You *have* jumped with Rajah and he's always been perfectly manageable," Grahame said in an undertone. Veronica tapped her foot.

"Dhulling, need we go into it all over again? I told you Rajah was excitable from the very start, and I wasn't going to make a fool of myself at the first fence. And anyway, you needn't sound so damn superior! You didn't excel yourself, I assure you. You gave Nabob's mouth a frightful tug over the gate, and your bowler looked too silly for *words* bobbing about——" She broke off, suddenly aware of our presence, disconcerted.

"Oh, hello, Carol! I—um, just saying how odd poor Grahame's hat looked. Congratulations, Pierre! You had a clear round, didn't you? What fun! I did envy you on such a lamb of a horse. I must say Rajah is usually like that, but sometimes he gets quite out of hand. And that wretched Amos——"

But all tempers are greatly soothed by a little nourishment. Sharp voices were mellowed, more civility observed, and an approach at tolerance was made by the majority. While we stirred our coffee, I overheard the stout matron pronounce her verdict on the sausage rolls:

"My dear Mrs Monksfoote, I've been told these rolls are of your baking and I must tell you they are the most delicious things I've tasted in years. How *do* you do it? So crisp!"

I saw Veronica tuck a forgiving geranium in Grahame's buttonhole, replacing the wilted carnation. I was even gladdened to see that Michael Fawcett and Basil Harker, who had chewed their salad in mutual exile, were sought out by their wives in time to share the chocolate gateau.

The juvenile riding contest took place in the afternoon.

"We feel that this event should be of a very brief duration," Mr Fanshawe had stated, "to avoid the likelihood of boredom among the adult spectators, and to obviate the possibility of—er—tantrums among the young entrants."

He then took up a sheet of paper and read out a list of some fifteen names. He read the list on a note of inquiry, glancing from time to time over his spectacles.

Four corpulent ponies, their juvenile riders wearing expressions of unutterable gloom, stood in a ragged line at the entrance of the arena. Several anxious-faced parents hastened across to Mr Fanshawe and, after a whispered consultation, he cleared his throat and announced that, owing to unfortunate accidents, eleven of the competitors would be unable to enter. He stressed the word unfortunate. One imagined a scene of havoc in the paddock—a stampede of ponies; broken reins; terrified cries; prostrate little forms lying face down in the trampled grass; weeping mothers. Imagination plays morbid games with half-unwilling delight.

But shortly after this distressing announcement eleven sullen children, with their stern-faced parents, approached us with looks of cold indifference, and with their appearance the noisy speculations ceased.

Among the four glowering entrants was little Angela on the Slug. To the horror of her companions she began to kick and swing her legs, calling: "Come on, Slug! Come *on*!"

"You can't start *now*! The bell hasn't gone, you'll be disqualified!" cried a little boy.

"I've got to start now," replied Angela. "If I start when the bell goes, it'll be too late."

Mr Fanshawe addressed himself to the megaphone once more. "The forthcoming event is in the nature of an obedience test. By which we imply the obedience of the pony to the child—not of the child to the pony! Ha, ha, ah, hum. The test is, in effect, one of elementary dressage. When I ring my bell, the children are to *walk* their ponies forward in a *straight* line, till ordered to trot. They will trot in this formation till ordered to halt. Each child will then be called out in turn to test the obedience of his or her pony. They will walk their ponies forward three paces, break into a trot, describing a circle to the left. At a given command they will urge their ponies into a *slow* canter, at which pace they will complete the circle. They will halt and rein back two paces, then return to their place at a walk. Now, boys and girls, as you know you are each going to make a circle to the *left*, so, when you are cantering, with which leg should your pony lead?"

Two of the small entrants looked with amazement from Mr Fanshawe to their parents. One little boy, Timothy Putters-Brooke, called shrilly: "The near fore, sir!" But Angela looked at Mr Fanshawe with scorn and said: "The front ones, of course."

"Come, come!" said Mr Fanshawe and rang his bell.

Timothy Putters-Brooke moved forward at a sedate walk; Joanna Monksfoote and her pony moved backwards till they met the fence behind them; and Clara Hayworth's pony pivoted round in a tight circle. The Slug remained where he was, chewing his bit.

There was an immediate surge forward of stricken parents, but they were quickly reproved on the megaphone and forced to retire, murmuring indignantly to each other.

Mr Fanshawe reminded the children that this was a test of obedience. The ragged line was formed once more, and the bell rung. This time Timothy, Joanna and Clara responded and only Angela remained behind. "Use your *legs*!" Mr Fanshawe bellowed, whereupon Angela slipped both feet out of the stirrup-irons and moved her legs energetically, as though pedalling a bicycle. The Slug seemed to smile. He moved forward in a purposeful manner.

"Trot!"

The ragged line increased its pace to a shambling movement.

"Halt!"

Angela's legs obeyed, but the Slug rolled inexorably forward. The pair were ignored by Mr Fanshawe, who now concentrated on the three remaining competitors.

When Timothy, Joanna and Clara had completed the exercise with varying degrees of success, the Slug was still exploring the outer limits of the arena, determined and unhurried as a mechanical toy that is wound up and circles the floor, propelled by unseen wheels within. Throughout this prosaic tour Angela called in a loud voice: "Stop! *Stop!* Stop, stop, stop, you fat slug!" At length, goaded beyond endurance by the amusement of the spectators of which she was fully aware, she stood up in her stirrups with her underlip thrust forward and eyes narrowed. Then she swooped down with bared teeth and sank them into the Slug's neck.

The announcement of Timothy Putters-Brooke as winner of the event went by unnoticed, for everyone was watching the Slug with gleeful terror. He flung up his hind legs, precipitating Angela over his shaggy head, and began to crop the short grass, oblivious of the screams and inquiries, advice and solicitations that went on about him.

Mr Fanshawe was at last forced to take notice of the fourth competitor in the juvenile riding contest. He hovered by helplessly while Irma gathered her child in her arms, tragic-faced.

"My dear Mrs Dutoit, this is unfortunate, most unfortunate!" said Mr Fanshawe, inadequately. Angela opened her eyes, which till he spoke had been screwed tightly shut.

She recognised the Native Commissioner as the perpetrator of her disgrace.

"You fat, ugly man, I *hate* you! Silly old show-off! Smelly fish! Daddy says you're a little tin god! Smelly, fat, tin god ... *Daddy* said so!"

"I believe she's concussed," said Irma Dutoit faintly in the silence which followed.

## CHAPTER SEVEN

TOWARDS the end of December Pierre and I became infected with the festive spirit and discussed the possibilities of giving a party.

"We would invite everyone in Dzokuti, of course, and also some of the farming people," said Pierre with enthusiasm. "Do you think we could cope with about twenty people? The living-room is a bit small, but they could overflow on to the veranda. The thing is how extravagant can we afford to be?"

"Well, we could stipulate that beer will be the only drink. And as far as the food goes I could stretch a few tins of sardines quite far if I make the canapés small enough. And the native eggs are quite cheap. . . ."

"Sounds rather dismal, doesn't it?"

"Very!"

"Darling, let's really make it worth while! We can be frightfully economical afterwards—just live on potatoes, and things. . . ."

"Oh, *yes*! Let's have mushrooms. Lots of tins of those black Leicestershire mushrooms . . . and oily black olives."

"And those fat, tinned shrimps! And asparagus. . . ."

"Caviare!"

"Prawns!"

We consulted a calendar and drew a ring around Friday, December 22nd. An aerial view of our sequestered little outpost would reveal the extent of its isolation—an atoll with clustered roofs of tin and thatch surrounded by an undulating sea of blue-green wilderness. Unravelling itself over the waves like a pale orange thread was the road that led to civilisation—a tenuous contact, and one which was all too easily severed in the wet season, when driving grey sheets of rain effaced the blue-green hills, and converging rivulets turned the earth into a soggy quagmire.

If the aerial onlookers were to arrive on a Thursday, and to suspend themselves patiently above this lonely clearing, they would observe, in due course, the beetle-like approach of a bus creeping along the road to Dzokuti. In this manner, jolting and lurching their way from Salisbury, our weekly supplies and the precious canvas mail-bags were delivered.

With the arrival of supplies on Thursday—paraffin-run refrigerators being of a temperamental nature—Friday was generally accepted as the day for entertaining.

On the morning of the twenty-second our cottage quaked at the violence with which Langton brandished his broom and duster. A family of geckos were banished and flannel-bodied wall-spiders ran for their lives. Brass door knobs were freed from verdigris. Pilchard lost his foothold on the floors. The venerable boards had been thickly smeared with polish to restore something of their former shine. When Langton had completed this particular task, however, and risen groaning from his wrinkled knees, I was rather afraid that the exercise had been a failure. Irma Dutoit would have described the floor as a disgusting, filthy mess. We also evicted a frog from its favourite haunt beneath a bookcase. Langton did suggest that the frog could "Watch 'im party", but the frog's pallid stomach palpitated at the notion and I placed it under a mango tree, where it stretched its lips into a nervous smile and said: "Squolk!"

Langton moved about the pantry with a strange mixture of self-importance and an awe amounting to reverence. Never before had he seen such an array of delicacies, and never, while he remained in our employ, was he likely to see such splendour again. Pink shrimps curled in creamy sauce, vol-au-vent cases in their dozens awaited the mushroom filling, and canapés were endless: smoked salmon, asparagus tips, caviare, anchovies, Camembert. Only the despised sardine was excepted.

I was happily squeezing lemon juice when a message came. An African constable stood to attention outside the kitchen door with a folded slip of paper.

"Darling there have been two sudden deaths at a kraal in the reserve Billy and I going there now investigate may be late lunch."

Ten minutes later Jennifer appeared with her hair in curling pins.

"Well, my hair's all set for your party," she said, "but I've a hunch that the party is going to be postponed."

"Postponed? Why, Pierre just said that they may be late for lunch. The party isn't till tonight."

"Pierre was being remarkably optimistic. This is the sort of thing that happens when you plan a party. You'll get used to it."

Making light of Jennifer's gloom I led her to the pantry

and was gratified to hear her startled: "Oh! Scrumptious!"
But pessimism won.

"Fortunately I think most of it will keep," she said, "except
the pastry; you'll have to make all those little puff things
again."

When she departed, shaking her scarf-wrapped head and
mumbling: "You'll get used to it," I returned to the kitchen
and squeezed lemons with fanatical vigour.

As the afternoon advanced, my party preparations lost
some of their original fervour. Baboushka came out of hiding
with cobwebs on his nose, and condescended to take a saucer
of milk. Langton retired behind the prison for a quiet smoke.

At four o'clock Pierre returned. "Sorry about the party,
darling. . . . Unless you have it without us. Billy will be taking
statements till the cows come home, and I've got to take
these corpses all the way to the native clinic at Ruwalo for
post-mortems. They have to be done today because the doctor
is giving evidence in a case at High Court tomorrow. Attend-
ing post-mortems is one of the more unpleasant sides of a
policeman's life."

"Corpses? Where are they?"

"In the Land-Rover. Three of them. Another died while
we were there. Billy and I think it's mushrooms, but it may
be witchcraft poisoning. We couldn't get a thing out of the
entire kraal. Old Sergeant Marufu almost resorted to
violence, but you know the way they just close up and refuse
to say a word. No one admitted to eating mushrooms and
no one admitted to dealings with a witchdoctor. There were
mostly only women and piccanins about as the men were out
working. Depressing scene—the piccanins wandering about
looking terrified and the women all in a huddle, mourning."

Without Pierre and Billy, I decided, the party would be
more in the nature of an Irish wake.

"Couldn't I come with you?" I asked.

"Forty-four miles, with three corpses in the back?"

"I know, but to stay here would be worse—sitting about smoking, looking at all those blasted shrimps and things. I can ask Jennifer to let everyone know the party has been postponed. . . ."

"All right. Come if you like. There seem to be quite a crowd of wives, and mothers and aunts in the back with the corpses, and the poor wretches will keep up a shrill and pro-longed wail all the way to the clinic."

Before we left we lunched late and despondently on shrimps and stuffed olives. The Leicestershire mushrooms had lost their appeal. We drove for some miles in a grim silence. The festive spirit had long since evaporated.

"You think it was mushrooms they ate?" I shouted above the noise of the Land Rover's engine.

"Yes. The mushrooms are coming out now. Most natives know which ones are edible but they can make mistakes. There was another piccanin at the kraal who was sick when we were there. I think he'll pull through. If he was going to die, he'd have done so before now, judging by the speed with which the other three apparently succumbed. They'd com-plained of pains and vomited and died all within the space of an hour. I don't think it's witchcraft poison, though we've had vague reports of an old *muroyi** in the district."

We came upon a stretch of road that was badly corrugated. I looked back through the open partition behind my head and saw three prostrate figures beneath flimsy grey blankets bouncing stiffly on the straw-covered floor of the vehicle. Their mourners rearranged the blankets over the rigid faces, and clapped hands and wailed with a new intensity.

The sun was setting when we drove up to the Ruwalo clinic. We stopped beside an austere building with green-gauzed windows and half-open double doors through which

* *Muroyi* : Shona for sorcerer or witch.

I glimpsed a sinister concrete slab on the floor. We had been preceded by the battered old car belonging to the Government medical officer. Dr Brodie came to the door, drying his hands with extreme thoroughness on a towel. He had the type of face which is impossible to describe because one sees it so often that the features have no significance. It was homely. He also looked very tired.

Pierre introduced us. "My wife felt like—er—going for a drive," he said lamely. Dr Brodie nodded.

"Quite. I'm afraid all this is going to take rather a long time. You wouldn't care to watch, Mrs de Choisy? Some people find it interesting. No? Quite!"

While he spoke two African clinic orderlies removed the blanketed bodies on a stretcher. Pierre followed Dr Brodie, who was still drying his hands, into the building and the doors closed behind them. The women who had accompanied the corpses sat on the ground beside the Land-Rover, gazing at the closed doors with dumb resignation.

Clinic patients drifted over with friendly curiosity to hear the bereaved women's story of death. The listeners murmured their sympathy and stayed to relate their own family tragedies. Some were pregnant women, some piccanins with festering sores on their legs, or eyes half-closed and watering with opthalmia. There were a large number of patients and relatives of patients in residence. They sat about the clinic grounds, the men squatting on their heels, the women with legs outstretched before them, talking idly or gazing vacantly into space.

When the sky darkened and crickets trilled in the shadows, the women lit small fires, cracking twigs and kneeling to blow on the smouldering embers. Sparks scattered in the velvet sky and the brown faces turned to a glowing bronze in the restless light of the flames. Thick maize-meal porridge was stirred in the pots. Babies bawled and were hushed. A hoary patriarch with one leg in plaster hobbled by with a dish, maundering to himself. A little boy ran past, stopping suddenly to rewind a trailing, dirty bandage on his foot. A young woman with bandaged eyes sat motionless with her hands in her lap, the whiteness of the bandage severing her face in the dark.

At last the thin line of light that escaped below the double doors expanded and illumined the surrounding trees. Dr Brodie stood silhouetted in the open doorway, drying his hands on a towel.

"Well, I'm pleased to have made your acquaintance, Mrs de Choisy," he said. "Perhaps next time we meet will be more—um—a happier occasion. Quite. Well, good night." He gave his hands a final rub and turned to go. He hesitated and turned back. "Oh, and the compliments of the season to you!" he said.

"What was the verdict?" I asked Pierre as we drove away.

"He's pretty certain it was mushrooms. But of course we can't be definite until we have the confirmation of the Government analyst. We'll be sending the stomachs along. They're all separately bottled in three preserving jars I borrowed from Jennifer."

Late that night we sat at our candle-lit table, eating asparagus tips and caviare with pensive speculation.

"Billy calls this sort of thing 'Exigencies of the Force'," said Pierre.

\*　　　\*　　　\*

When Pierre was constrained to spend the greater part of the night investigating some misdeed in a distant compound, or when I hurried to answer the telephone on a Sunday morning in the happy anticipation of a social call and was met instead with an urgent appeal to the Dzokuti police by some anxious member of the public, I was very conscious of Billy Burkitt's "Exigencies of the Force". But as the months passed I learned to treat such incidents with philosophic acceptance. It is the minor irritant which demands a greater tolerance.

My early morning visit to the grass-sheltered thunder-box was not such a simple expedition as might be supposed, for a small tool-shed stood directly in my line of approach.

Every morning a helmeted African gaol guard would importantly flourish a jangle of keys before the unappreciative faces of his little band of prisoners. The tool-shed would be unlocked and he would distribute *badzas** and sickles in a pompous silence. This ceremony was not performed with any punctuality. I was therefore obliged to loiter at the corner of the cottage, ears pricked for the ring and clank of the implements to fade away, before venturing forth. If all was quiet I might safely presume that the company had departed. I was sometimes fortunate enough to make both the outward and return journey unobserved. Less rarely I would reach the first clump of banana palms in furtive haste, only to be met half-way by the advancing party. The ever-courteous guard would then halt his entire retinue, come to attention with a Teutonic stamp of his feet, and bid me good morning. Having returned his greeting with unfelt enthusiasm, I would assume an even less-felt nonchalance and saunter toward the grass enclosure, well aware that every prisoner was watching my progress with interest.

They were not the only witnesses to my morning excursion. The prisons faced my approach, and in the centre of each prison door was set a small, barred aperture. Prisoners awaiting trial would while away their hours of confinement by viewing the activities of the police camp through these narrow slots. My own entries to and exits from the grass en-

* *Badza* : Shona for a hoe.

closure came under the heading of "Camp Life". Every morning a pair of curious eyes was glued to each aperture, marking my movements. Should I glance in their direction, the dark eyes would roll till the whites showed before vanishing in the inner gloom.

Another affair to be endured was the police radio schedule. We had a scratched and scarred wireless—the property of the police and part of our inheritance from Pierre's bachelor days, when our cottage was known as the "Single Quarters". Over my coffee-and-cigarette breakfast I liked to give the eight o'clock B.B.C. news relayed from London my full attention; it was the only occasion when the outside world penetrated Dzokuti's serene insularity. But the police morning radio schedule coincided with what the B.B.C. had to relate. The technicalities of the matter were incomprehensible to me, but by some peculiar mischance the well-enunciated voice of Michael Ashby or Hugh Tattersall suffered continual interference. This necessitated a piecing together of fragments and trying to conjecture the whole. The announcement that Mr Bulganin had sent another message to President Eisenhower on the subject of a summit conference would be disconcertingly interrupted by Pierre's voice:

"Dzokuti to ZEF2, Dzokuti to ZEF2, do you read me? Over." *Beep*. Michael Ashby would continue unruffled: "In America's reply to the Soviet proposals it was stated that——"

"Two certified non-criminal lunatics and escort arriving Salisbury 1 p.m. Arrange transport. Over." *Beep*.

There was also the tea shuttle service. All visitors calling at the police camp, no matter what the hour of the day, were served with tea—a long-established tradition. The visitors were numerous: farmers, missionaries, Native Engineering Department representatives, Government surveyors, even prospective big-game hunters. The big-game hunters were invariably callow youths, equipped with bravado and tins of bully-beef, armed with a light rifle and trustingly sure of finding fresh drinking water wherever the whim of their one-man, motor-bike safari would lead them. These pre-doomed Nimrods would be sent home by Billy with chastening advice and a mollifying cup of tea.

Very often such demands for tea would follow upon each other without pause and Langton would hurriedly rinse the sugary dregs from the cups already on the tray. The promptness with which he executed these orders gave me grave misgivings. That the kettle ever reached boiling point I very much doubted, and I even suspected that the same tea leaves were stewed more than once. The brew must often have been abominable, but we never received any complaints.

The frequently recurring episode of the tie, however, was one little vexation which I successfully surmounted. A surprising number of European farmers in the district, unaware of the dignity required in court, would arrive as Crown witnesses to give evidence against some scampish farm labourer attired in their customary khaki shorts and shirt— the shirt open-necked and tie-less. Such an appearance would undoubtedly have met with the embarrassingly caustic disapproval of Mr Fanshawe. When the call for a tie was relayed from the office I would hurry into the bedroom muttering: "A tie! A tie!" and Pierre's wardrobe was invariably left in a windswept turmoil from my frantic search and final selection, for I always made an effort to suit the prospective wearer. The tie rummage came to an end when I demanded that Pierre choose one of his less-favoured ties and leave it permanently draped over a nail on the kitchen wall.

*       *       *

Unless necessity dictated otherwise, court was normally held on Fridays. Pierre suggested that I attend one Friday when no case would be reviewable and my presence would be least likely to disconcert the crusty Mr Fanshawe.

Putting on a drooping garden hat which I hoped would suffice, I accompanied Pierre down the road to the court-room, Pilchard trotting gaily beside us. Every Friday a noisy multitude of Africans gathered outside the courtroom, await-ing their turn to take part in one or another of the never-ending grievances which gave spice to their existence. Their bicycles and babies and scavenging dogs lent colour to the scene and their arguments and accusations were interposed with the abandoned laughter of their habitually cheerful temperaments.

The courtroom was detached from the Native Depart-ment offices. A smartly uniformed messenger opened the glass doors for us and we stepped into the small, plain-furnished room. At the opposite end was the door by which Mr Fanshawe would enter.

Too large to be stored in a cupboard, exhibits from past cases crowded one corner: bicycles; intriguing lumps of rock (which Pierre explained were the distressing exhibits from a case of infanticide); broken clay pots; and a cheap cardboard suitcase that had once held stolen goods.

Pilchard pranced in with us. With punctilious sniffs he had established a homely familiarity with every object in the room, and the wooden panel of the witness box was selected on which to leave intimation of his visit. He was hastily removed.

Pierre brought a chair for me and we talked in undertones. He had two exhibits which he laid on the table before him—a gnarled stick and a vicious knobkerry. An African con-stable was instructed to summon the first accused, a stocky, sullen man named Mjenje. Mjenje stood scowling in the dock and the constable stationed himself at the glass doors with

feet apart and hands behind his back. Pierre and I and
Mjenje and the constable waited in patient silence and
listened to his Worship stirring his tea in a neighbouring
office. Flies buzzed drowsily on the window panes.

Presently we heard the sound of a throat being cleared in
accompaniment to the scrape of a chair, and Mr Fanshawe's
face appeared at a window. It expressed acute irritation and
was withdrawn. Fearing that my presence might be the cause,
I was relieved to hear his stentorian bellow for Pemba, the
court interpreter. Pemba was berated for failing to be at his
post. According to court procedure the interpreter was to
anticipate Mr Fanshawe's entry by standing ready at the
door, opening it the moment Mr Fanshawe knocked for
admittance. The ceremony was now observed and Mr
Fanshawe strode into the room, Pierre simultaneously calling
for "Silence in court!" I stood respectfully with the court till
his Worship was seated, while Pilchard pressed his black nose
to the glass doors with a whimpered appeal to my better
nature.

Pierre remained standing, and commenced the prosecution
by confirming the name of the accused and charging him
with Common Assault. This through the African interpreter,
Pemba, who stood erect in his brass-buttoned uniform, straining to mark each word, his brown face glistening.

Pierre asked the accused whether he wished to plead guilty
or not. Mjenje pleaded guilty, and at once launched into a
rambling account of his action.

What consequence the cramped and rural courtroom
lacked was well amended by the sententious mien of Mr
Fanshawe himself. Glaring at the accused over his spectacles,
he gave emphasis to each word: "You are merely asked
whether you plead guilty or not. Should you wish to make
an explanation, you will be given the opportunity of doing so
later. Do you plead guilty or not guilty?"

This was hastily interpreted to the undismayed Mjenje who raked the courtroom with suspicious eyes, and after some reflection pleaded guilty without further embellishment.

The constable at the door summoned the complainant, a small African woman called Dora. She shuffled in barefoot, wearing a shapeless, ragged frock, her right hand importantly swathed in bandages. Cowed by the solemn hush and the strange surroundings, she placed her forefinger between her lips and, sucking it vigorously, was led to the witness box. She was sworn in and, gaining confidence, glanced provocatively at the surly Mjenje.

The animated discussions and unbridled guffaws of the throng outside the courtroom had gradually increased in volume and before proceeding further Mr Fanshawe was compelled to dispatch his interpreter with a request for more restraint. The tumult, while it did not altogether subside, was conducted in a lower key.

From a tangle of irrelevant details, contradictions and reiterations the particulars of the complainant's story were patiently extricated. At one point the interpreter, complainant and accused wrangled with heat in their own tongue, which caused the irascible Mr Fanshawe considerable discomfort.

Throughout the proceedings Mr Fanshawe's pen scratched steadily down a sheet of foolscap, recording the evidence. He wrote with slow deliberation and during the prolonged pauses when he interrupted the prosecution to complete a statement in his laborious hand dissonant sounds intruded upon the silence within. The abrasive crunch of a car's wheels on the gravel outside; Derek Vaughn's loud, metallic laugh answering Michael Fawcett's low-toned murmur; the click-clicking of a typewriter that seemed to reproach the warm idleness of the summer day.

According to the evidence produced by Dora, she had stepped down to the river one evening to fill her water-pots when the accused had approached her with a stick in his hand. Upbraiding her for having ill-treated his daughter, he had given force to his reproof by inflicting several blows on the arm which she had flung up in order to shield her face.

Dora denied having ill-treated Mjenje's daughter. She had brought the gnarled stick, which now lay on the table before Pierre, as evidence of her trouncing. Upon its being exhibited in court she excitedly declared that it was the very stick with which the accused had belaboured her. Mjenje disagreed. The stick had been a much longer one, he said.

He was asked if he had anything further to say. He had. The interpreter translated his final invective:

"She must be a woman with the strength of a man. She has said I hit her very hard. She has said I hit her so many times that she could not remember how many. Yet all she has to show from this great beating is one bandaged hand!"

Dora looked at him obliquely and curled her lip. She was replaced by a witness, a stick-legged child who pattered in with mouth agape. The little witness, whose undersized appearance probably belied her age, was guided to the box by the interpreter and impressed with the fact that she must not tell lies. She received this injunction with open mouth; indeed it remained open for the length of her evidence, which was brief.

Did she know that man?

"*Ongu*,"* she squeaked.

Did he live in her kraal?

"*Ongu*."

Where was Dora on the evening of Wednesday the twentieth, last week?

"With me by the Kokwe river."

* *Ongu* : Shona for "yes".

Did anything happen?

"*Ongu.*"

What happened?

"Mjenje came. He was angry. He shouted at Dora and he hit her hand with a stick."

Pierre lifted the stick from his table. Did she see this stick?

"*Ongu.*"

Was this the stick which he used?

"*Ongu.*"

Was it not perhaps a longer stick?

"*Ongu.*"

When the doors were opened for her, Pilchard strove to reach me by worming his way between her legs, but his tail was caught by the horror-stricken constable, who thrust him firmly without.

The prosecution declared that it had no further witnesses to call. The accused was unable to produce a witness himself, and had nothing further to say.

Mr Fanshawe adjusted his spectacles.

"I find you guilty of common assault and sentence you to pay a fine of one pound or to serve a period of two weeks in gaol."

At this point the rejected Pilchard sat on his haunches and howled with the high, quavering anguish and penny-whistle penetration of which only a puppy is capable. Mr Fanshawe's bifocal spectacles swung outraged in my direction and I vacated the courtroom, my guilt far surpassing that of the unrepentant Mjenje.

## CHAPTER EIGHT

BESIDES their remunerative store, the Harkers owned a butchery which was no less prosperous.

"Who'd have thought I'd ever find *myself* doing this sort of thing?" said Betty one morning as I watched her chopping bones for Pilchard with the deftness born of long practice. Her remark was tinged with apologetic pride—or was it a proud apology? Her question, however, was rhetorical; though with a backdrop of glistening slabs of beef that swung from their iron hooks her own soigné appearance was inapposite, she nevertheless boned foreribs and judged the weight of her cuts with an experienced eye.

But apart from the flies that alighted on the butchery's blood-stained counter, there was one more persistent fly in the ointment of its flourishing trade. As the profits of the butchery increased with the passing years, so the building which housed it declined and all but fell. The last traces of whitewash faded; the cracks multiplied; the door swung loose on its hinges; and the torn gauze on the windows yawned ever wider in mocking parody of the sanitary screen it had once afforded.

With growing frequency, both in his official capacity when ordering the weekly meat ration for the prison, and during his social calls, when he employed a more bantering tone, Billy Burkitt had remarked upon the unsanitary conditions of the butchery. The official rebuke met with Mrs Harker's barely disguised hostility, and the social one with affected incredulity—to be treated as a light-hearted jest between old friends that is at once indulged and dismissed.

Billy Burkitt had no intention of dismissing the matter. "Flies!" he exclaimed one day with a shudder of revulsion. "Ye gods and little fishes! The place is *black* with 'em—well anyway, quite enough to make it unhealthy. Damn sure those scales aren't accurate either. . . . I've a good mind to —yes, I will, dammit! I shall inform her this afternoon that if the place isn't improved within a month I'll have the Health Inspector along and she'll probably be prosecuted under the Public Health Regulations. That'll shake her!"

Jennifer and I awaited his return with impatience, and when he did return were shameless in our clamour for a full report of the manner in which Betty Harker received his news. Billy displayed that exasperating masculine inability to recount events in detail.

"She exploded," he said briefly.

"Oh dear!" said Jennifer. "Unless I'm very diplomatic this is going to lead to a—what's the word? A blood feud!"

"I don't think any diplomacy on your part will alter the

situation," said Billy, smiling and tugging his moustache. "Judging from Betty's face, we must be prepared for a breaking-off of negotiations, a recall of ambassadors—in fact, a declaration of war between the Harkers and the Burkitts."

The following day I was aware of an excessive amount of activity in Dzokuti whose dusty lanes so seldom boasted of traffic. I glimpsed the sleek bulges of a black Buick gleaming outside the Native Commissioner's house. Presently it appeared at the house of the Clerk of the Court. Throughout the morning the revving of its engine, changing of its gears and echoing slam of its doors startled the inhabitants of the drowsy little outpost.

Shortly before midday the Buick nosed up our own drive, its chromium flashing brazenly in the sun. Betty Harker emerged.

"My dear, I won't stay more than a minute," she said as I approached. "Of course, you know why I've come?" I professed my ignorance in the matter.

"Well, it all boils down to the fact that Billy Burkitt is being very childish and silly and I refuse to be ridden over rough-shod. Of course, it's all absolute nonsense, but he declares my butchery is unsanitary! Isn't it too ridiculous? When I think of all the charming policemen I've dealt with in the past . . . Sergeant Moreton, and Sergeant Warrick, and dear Sergeant Davis . . . and to think it's come to this! Of course, I said to Basil there's only one thing to do and that's to see everyone in Dzokuti and ask them to sign a petition in our favour—I've drawn it up myself—to the effect that they have all dealt at my butcher shop for a considerable time and see no cause for complaint. I feel perfectly justified in doing this. Everyone here has bought our meat without a murmur. If Billy carries on in this officious manner in spite of public opinion, I can't answer for the consequences, but I feel he may very well jeopardise his career in the police force. Believe me, these sort of things don't sound well at Headquarters!"

Mrs Harker glared at me in the strong sunlight and my suggestion that we went indoors was unheeded. Three ragged piccanins were attracted by her impassioned tones and loitered at the roadside, nudging each other and whispering and covering their smiles with their narrow brown hands. But Mrs Harker was not aware of them.

"My dear, I'm sure you won't be offended that I called on you last of all," she said, "but you are the newcomer here and I felt it better to make my visits in order of precedence. I called on Daphne Fanshawe first, of course, then Brenda Fawcett and Irma Dutoit. I managed to see Derek and John in their offices, though Michael Fawcett was out. I don't include Belinda, as she's just a visitor, and of course I didn't as much as *look* in the direction of the Burkitts' house—I'm sure Jennifer must be at the bottom of this!" Betty Harker spoke with such energy that she was frequently compelled to pause for breath. During one of these intervals I asked with impolite curiosity if she had secured all the signatures she sought.

"Well, no, as a matter of fact—no, not quite. I find people are always very willing to express a *verbal* opinion but when it comes to actually *signing* something they become so spineless and indecisive that it makes one *seethe*. Of course, I know you're different, but really, it's been a most *exhausting* morning!"

I nodded in sympathy. "Was Mrs Fanshawe not—er?"

"Oh, Daphne Fanshawe was charming. I quite understood how difficult it was for her. After all, she is in a position quite different to the rest. I mean, she pointed out—well, not in so many words, but I could see what she meant—that her own signature would carry such weight as to make all the others

meaningless and unnecessary. I mean, after all, the N.C.'s
wife! She felt—and I could see her point of view—that a
petition *without* her signature would carry so much more
weight. I mean, if *she* signed it, everyone else would be bound
to follow suit. I want people to express their unprejudiced
opinion as to the cleanliness of my butchery. It was a most
far-sighted attitude of hers and I quite understood. She was
quite charming and said the flies *are* very bad at this time of
the year everywhere, what with the rains and everything."

"And was Mrs Fawcett not—er?"

"Oh, Brenda really tries my patience! It was quite impossible to pin her down. One minute she agreed that the last
sirloin she bought from me was very good and the next
minute she was all chilly and said how awkward it was for
her to become involved in what she called a personal issue
between myself and Billy Burkitt, because she and Michael
play bridge with the Burkitts every Thursday night. I confess
I was quite acid. I certainly wasn't going to *beg* her to sign it.
Then I went to see Irma Dutoit. The wretched woman was
positively odious! She said there's no smoke without a fire
and if the sergeant felt the butchery was unsanitary she
would have to order her meat from town as she couldn't risk
dear little Angy's health. I've never been so cross. Her sister
Belinda was there and of course tried to be tactful and said
one man's meat is another man's poison. Really! Then of
course Irma's husband is a fool. He treated the whole thing
as a joke. I can't imitate the appalling way he speaks but he
said: 'Ag, man, keep on the right side of the wife and the law
an' you can't go wrong!' So of course it was out of the question asking *him* to sign either."

"And Derek Vaughn?"

"Well, you know the sardonic manner Derek puts on. I
really didn't know whether he was serious or not, but he said
he'd been studying Buddhism and wanted his heart to be

untouched by worldly things or some such nonsense. He said Buddha forbade him to touch meat, so the matter was of no concern to him." Betty Harker drew a deep breath, pursed her lips and raised her eyebrows. "So there you are," she said. "At all events I'm sure *you* have no cause for complaint, my dear. I know the steak you had last week was a little tough but that *is* beside the point really, isn't it?"

It was an awkward situation. I had no little Angela to protect from infection and was not studying Buddhism. I was unable to assume the chilly front adopted by Brenda and I was not in the exalted position held by Mrs Fanshawe. My own signature would look very lonely and exposed on Mrs Harker's petition, and I had no wish to see it flourished before the genial Billy Burkitt.

"I can see how trying all this must be for you," I said, "but wouldn't it perhaps be better to avoid the unpleasantness and just get a few sheets of gauze for the door and windows and——" Betty Harker turned before I had completed my sentence and flung herself into the car. Had I not stepped hastily to one side I ran the risk of being run down in my own drive as the Buick swept haughtily past me, and the piccanins scattered with shrill cries of delighted terror. By lunchtime the dust had settled in the lanes again and Dzokuti's habitual drowsiness returned.

But the breach which widened between the Burkitts and the Harkers, and seemed as though it must engulf their old friendship, was healed over-night by an unexpected stroke of fate.

The shrill ring of the telephone awakened us at that time when light is seeping into the sky but the stars are not yet extinguished. The call was from District Headquarters, Salisbury. The Officer in Command was on the line. Serious rioting had broken out among the African mine workers on the Copper Belt in Northern Rhodesia. Sergeant Burkitt was commanded to leave Dzokuti at dawn to join a contingent of B.S.A. Police who were to be flown to the Copper Belt to assist Northern Rhodesian police in quelling the riot.

"This is the sort of thing I *hate*!" said Jennifer despondently stirring her tea. She had sent an appealing note requesting my company that morning. "The house seems awful lonely," she sighed; "I couldn't sleep after seeing Billy off at four o'clock this morning. Seems ages ago now."

"If it's any consolation, I'm sure Billy will enjoy the excursion hugely," I said. "Pierre seemed almost disappointed that he wasn't going, too."

"Oh, I know! Billy was like an excited schoolboy—packing his kit and rushing about! He will enjoy it. It's always the wives who suffer, sitting about and worrying. Still, I don't suppose it will be more than a few days."

There was a peremptory knock on the half-open door and Betty Harker swooped into the room. She beamed. Her pekingese struggled under one arm, and a colourful assortment of illustrated papers seemed in danger of escaping from the other.

"Jennifer, my dear, I hear you've become a grass widow! I know too well how boring it is. Basil is hardly ever away but I remember the last time he spent three days in town on business. I think the worst part was having no one to talk to in bed at night; you know, I do love lying in the dark and talking, I could go on for hours, I never get sleepy. Anyway, I've brought you some magazines, there are some very good knitting patterns in them. And my dear, I do hope you'll have dinner with us while Billy's away. Why not come up for lunch today and stay for tea?"

Thus was the hatchet mutually and unquestioningly buried—and the flies buzzed unmolested through the sagging butchery door.

Shortly after this carnivorous dispute the missionary Lewis Brocken paid us a visit, and delivered a sermon and a haunch of venison.

"I shot me a young kudu," he beamed, lifting his helmet and wiping his shining forehead with a handkerchief.

"*You* shot it?" Pierre teased him.

"Sure. It is written in the Book of Genesis that man will have dominion over the fish of the sea, and over the fowl of the air, and over the cattle, and over all the earth. Animals have no souls and I believe they were put upon the earth for the benefit of man."

Despite his generosity in bringing us a share of his spoils, I was drawn into the discussion and once more found myself questioning Lewis Brocken's unshakable beliefs. On this occasion science did not come to my rescue, but I was more familiar with the Book of Genesis.

"I'm not a vegetarian," I had to admit, "but I'm arguing on their behalf. It was written that we should have dominion over the fish, cattle, fowls and creepy-crawlies, but dominion means sovereignty or control. A ruler has dominion over his subjects but doesn't necessarily eat them. And there's no implication in the Book of Genesis that animals were intended to be eaten by us. Further to your quotation, it is written: 'Behold, I have given you every herb bearing seed, which is upon the face of all the earth, and every tree, in the which is the fruit of a tree yielding seed; to you it shall be for meat.' That sounds to me more like a vegetarian diet."

"Well, I sure am pleased to see you read the Book," replied Lewis, "but I think you're kinda splitting straws. The fact remains that animals have no souls and we have dominion over them."

Recalling Derek Vaughn's current interest in Buddhism, I tried a different angle. "The Buddhists," I began, ignoring the missionary's wince, "the Buddhists preach against taking

the life of anything living from an antelope to a beetle. With
them such mercy springs from the fear of killing a lost rela-
tive who may be travelling incognito, so to speak, in the
form of a beetle. Well, I think reincarnation quite possible—
in fact one could describe Christ's return to earth as a
reincarnation—and though I don't think reincarnation in
insect or animal form a very logical idea in relation to evolution, the compassionate preservation of life does seem logical.
And incidentally how can you be so certain that animals have
no souls?"

"Animals have no souls because they were not made in
God's image," said Lewis with unarguable finality. "As to
your point of the merciful preserving of life, well, I guess if
you carry that one to extremes you'll find yourself killing off
your fellow men by preserving the living germs and bacteria
that spread disease! And then what of the plants of the earth?
I reckon they come into the category of living things and so
in your terms cabbages must also be preserved. No, Mrs
de Choisy, perhaps one day when man becomes a perfect
being he'll be able to live without any other sustenance than
the love which feeds his heart but until that time comes we
must satisfy our bodily needs with the life that is given under
our dominion."

We could not but agree with such a sensible view, and
accepted his venison with all the more pleasure for the re-
moval of any doubts as to the rightness of its consumption.

Such a large haunch suggested, even demanded, a dinner
party. In a small outpost the movements of its inhabitants
are made common knowledge; we are all acquainted with
each other's engagements. Pierre and I were therefore aware
that the company of both Belinda Storm and Derek Vaughn
would be at our disposal the following evening. We had for
some time past discussed the complacent self-confidence of
Oliver Lindsay and felt a little rivalry would not be amiss.

We felt that Miss Storm's admiration for the physical beauties of the male might be advantageously superseded by an awakening regard for the intellect of the male. Despite his protestations to the contrary on the day of the Gymkhana, we persuaded ourselves that Derek might yet fall prey to the appeal of fresh simplicity—feminine innocence that would offset so well his own erudite satire.

We made our preparations. With all the tender exactitude of a Frenchman Pierre made the sauce. He tied an apron round his middle and hummed about the kitchen in a most endearing manner. Onions, garlic, a quantity of butter and sherry in lieu of red wine were blended with subtlety and muttered incantations. Other ingredients were stirred in with furtive secrecy when my back was turned. The result had an exquisite piquancy and Pierre called it *Sauce Macabre*.

With more bustle and less success I undertook to make a Russian cream. The recipe implored me to bring the mixture "*just* to the boil". It warned me that if the custard was overcooked the outcome of all my efforts would be an unappetising, curdled mass. I read this ominous postscript to the recipe while the custard was boiling, and when I returned to the stove I found an unappetising, curdled mass.

"*Tant pis*," said Pierre, "send up to the Harkers' store for a tin of peaches."

Somewhat humiliated, I slid the curdled mass into a basin for Pilchard and left Pierre in command of the kitchen.

Doubting the sincerity of Derek's recent conversion to Buddhism, I composed the following invitation:

"Dear Derek, Did you seek refuge in Buddha because you were weary of the hypocrisies of the social round, and in your new faith do you gain merit by abstaining from the carnivore's appetites? Or was it a momentary conversion?

A happy thought that came to you when under pressure—
and one which blew away in the smoke of the first stick of
incense you lit in gratitude for deliverance from the tempta-
tions of the Flesh and the tirades of the Woman? If the
latter was the case we'd be pleased to see you this evening,
when we hope you will share a leg of venison with us."

I wrote a more formal note to Miss Belinda Storm, and
another to Mrs Harker, requesting a tin of peaches. The
three notes, addressed to Mr Vaughn, Miss Storm and Mrs
Harker respectively, were also given marks of identity in
Langton's presence. Langton folded each note between
separate fingers, his dignified silence implying a complete
comprehension of my instructions.

The resulting confusion was inevitable. Having delivered
the invitation to Miss Storm, Langton's brief memory had
expired, and he betook himself to the store, where he felt the
remaining two notes could be sorted by Mrs Harker herself.
Yet I could not have foreseen that Mrs Harker's curiosity
would prompt her to peruse the contents of both the note
addressed to her and that bearing the address of Mr Vaughn.
That she did so was revealed in the terse note which she
subsequently addressed to me.

"Dear Carol, I have given your boy a tin of peaches and
charged it to your account. I am sure dear Derek will
enjoy your venison. I was unaware that I had exerted any
pressure when asking him to sign my petition, though I did
think his answer was rather affected. I am surprised that
you condone his childish attitude and can only forgive the
weak humour of your letter to him on the grounds that you
are very young yourself. Yours, Betty H."

This note was produced at the commencement of our

dinner party and, if it did not dampen our spirits, it served to break the ice.

Belinda arrived in a flurry of salmon pink flounces, her plump shoulders seductively exposed. Derek arrived with a lock of his blond hair drooping over his high, pale forehead, and a book of Confucian analects conspicuous in one hand. Perceiving Miss Storm in a corner of our sagging sofa, he pocketed the analects with a shrug of resignation.

"Still enjoying the salubrious airs of our secluded hamlet?" he asked Belinda with a humourless smile. She fingered her necklace nervously. "Sal——? Oh, I see! Yes, oh yes! It's ever such a jolly little place, isn't it?"

A small pause while we sipped our drinks and composed penetrating questions and shrewd observations. The spell was broken when our questions and observations tumbled forth.

*Belinda:* "I'm told you're a writer of verse, Mr Vaughn?"

*Pierre:* "I feel the witchcraft case we had today should have been a P.E."

*Myself:* "The natives are saying we must expect floods this season."

*Derek:* "I wonder if the still, small voice of Bertrand Russell on the question of atomic——"

We paused again, then smiled, apologised, and entreated one another to go on with what they were saying. Belinda was encouraged to continue. "What sort of verse do you like writing best?" she asked with a confidential smile. Hostility removed the customary drawl from Derek's speech and his reply was curt. "They don't rhyme," he said.

"Oh!"

"And I very much doubt if you could be entertained by them. Most of the stuff I write borders on the transcendental, if it doesn't actually wallow in it. And I don't waste my time with metrics."

F

Belinda was nettled by the sharpness of his tone and tossed her head, "If you mean they're not *love* poems, I happen to like the other kinds, too! But if it's the type of poetry where you just make patterns with the words I wouldn't even pretend to understand them."

Pierre caught my eye. Our plan was going awry. It was apparent that Derek was not enthralled by a julep of such ingenuous compound. It was also apparent that Belinda would find no comfort in the chill glow of the savant's lantern. Yet our own efforts to draw them into a discussion of more general and amiable topics were in vain. Derek persistently toyed with Belinda's artless remarks as a cat teases a quivering mouse. On the infrequent occasions when the point of his malice pierced its cloak of sarcasm, and the mouse shrank back, the cat would sheathe his claws and pat it with a soft, sly paw till it came forward again and, all unsuspecting, groomed its whiskers. But if his feline strategics at any time became ungracious, the mouse displayed its teeth and squeaked and bounced with such fearless energy that the cat blanched beneath his fur.

Pierre and I were tolerated as umpires rather than host and hostess. Our sparring guests dealt with poetry, the absurdity of women's fashions, the sentimentality of Victorian novelists, and any other subject in which Derek fancied he could snub the half-coquettish jocularity of his opponent, but in every instance he was frustrated, defeated by the very simplicity he sought to expose. Belinda closed the door on each succeeding subject with random comments so vague, so irrelevant, irrational and frivolous as to be unanswerable.

However, the contest had no deleterious effect upon Miss Storm's appetite. When, in reply to her wide-eyed inquiry, we found an illustration of a kudu with its long, spiralling horns, she sighed: "Oh, isn't he lovely! Poor beasty—we're eating you!" And bent over her second helping with un-diminished gusto. Derek said: "It quite terrifies me to think how easily I might have become a Buddhist! Who was it who said: 'Turtle soup is very wholesome, and so is venison'? Was it Thackeray in his *Memorials of Gormandising*, or is it something out of *Handley Cross*?"

"Mrs Beeton?" suggested Belinda indistinctly, savouring a mouthful.

After dinner, when Derek had unfolded his legs, and cupped his long back in an armchair, he allowed Belinda to bounce unrestrained on the sofa beside me, and gave us his views on more significant and weighty problems than those which he had disposed of before the venison appeared. He declared that Britain and America should abandon nuclear tests and drop the hot coal of atomic research before its combustible quality led inevitably to war. Russia, he said, would use their own atomic weapons merely as a threat to subdue us, for to wreck the countries they intended to occupy would be too, too utterly absurd. Two could play at the passive game of threats, he said. He impressed us with the imperative need for the Western powers to withstand the threats of Russia on the strength of their own superior atomic discoveries. When he found that he had led himself on a course that arrived at a point opposite to that of his original opinion, the heat of his argument cooled, and he stirred his coffee and addressed himself to Pierre.

"Why did you say that witchcraft case should be a P.E.?"

"Because the Crown's evidence is more than adequate to establish the accused's guilt," said Pierre, "and you haven't the jurisdiction to award her a sufficiently severe sentence."

Derek stroked his long nose. "I'm not happy about it myself, but I haven't found any *A.G.* circulars or anything else concerning that section of the Act."

"What is all this about a witchcraft case?" said Belinda, who had been listening with her mouth slightly open, "Is it *real* witchcraft? Sounds awfully spooky. Do tell!"

"It's more sordid than spooky," said Derek, "and there isn't really any witchcraft involved. It's one of these eternal cases of one native 'wrongfully and unlawfully imputing' someone else for 'the use of non-natural means in causing sickness and death'. And, like most of them, it's a rather garbled story."

"Oh, but tell us! What happened?"

Had her eager inquiry been made before dinner, Belinda would have been told that the case could not possibly amuse her, that it was all a little nauseating and not worth repeating; but repletion had dulled the trenchant blade of his tongue.

"Well, to begin with," he said, "there's a rather revolting native superstition which has it that if a person is possessed of a certain evil spirit he can eat the flesh of a dead and buried person without suffering any ill effect——"

"Oh! Oh, I say! You're pulling my leg, you beast!"

Derek raised his eyebrows at her. "I wouldn't attempt to pull your leg," he said dryly. "It's quite a well-known affair, they call it *shave re uroyi*. A certain African female named Murashaya is guilty of contravening section three of the Witchcraft Suppression Act, chapter forty-six."

"Oh, how awful! You mean she actually ate dead bodies?"

"No, no, no. This Murashaya merely got a bee in her unpleasant bonnet over the mysterious illness and subsequent death of her husband's second wife. She was the first and elder wife—he had three—and a decided crone. After the younger woman had died, Murashaya went about saying she was possessed of an evil spirit and pointing out five other women of her kraal as witches. She accused them of using unnatural means in causing the death of the second wife and, not satisfied with that, went on to say they had all commanded her to dig up the body and eat it, and offered to help in its consumption themselves."

"And then?"

"Well, apparently she told her husband all about it and he told the kraal's headman. The old headman asked her to repeat the accusation in front of the five women. She did so and also added a great many elaborations to the effect that previous deaths in the kraal were all due to the sorcery of these five 'witches' and that a great many of the corpses had been gobbled up in the process. A lot of gruesome nonsense."

"Oh, but then she's just been telling naughty stories. Why should her sentence be so severe?"

"Because, my dear Miss Storm, among the more primitive Africans who populate this district naughty lies of that nature can have very nasty consequences. If anyone dies a natural death and the natives are ignorant as to the disease which caused the death, they immediately suspect witchcraft. And in the past a great many innocent people have been labelled as 'witches' responsible for someone's death in much the same manner as Murashaya accused her five fair companions of witchery, only in her instance she is no one of importance and her accusations carry no weight in the kraal. But in other cases the imputation *has* carried weight and the unfortunate woman, unable to prove her innocence, has been 'erased' as they say in spy stories, usually by poison."

"Oh, isn't it shameful. Irma told me about the Blacks—the natives I mean—being so dirty and lazy in the kitchen but she never told me anything like *that*!"

"It's not really all that long ago that we were shoving old beldames into the Thames ourselves, to see if they were witches," Derek pointed out. Belinda giggled but pursued the subject.

"Oh, I know we did," she said, "but there was no one to

tell us any better. These natives can turn to the white people for guidance and I'd have thought that they'd find *our* magic so clever that they'd forget about all their silly old evil spirits and witchdoctors and things. I mean, even here they know about telephones and cars and aeroplanes and things . . . ?"

Derek shook his head. "You must remember that fear is the strongest emotion," he said, "especially fear of an intangible evil. Anger is an emotion that can't be maintained indefinitely, it degenerates into sulks, you know; but fear is always with them, the hereditary fear of their 'silly old evil spirits' that goes much too deep to be forgotten with the advent of cars and telephones. Take a case that happened quite recently in this district. An African who works on a farm near here was going away for some reason for a short spell, leaving his wife behind. He doubted his wife's fidelity, so he resorted to the use of an African medicine which is commonly known, though I can't remember what they call it. Apparently the idea is that if the woman takes this concoction, though she herself is quite unaffected by it, any man with whom she may commit adultery will suffer the consequences—become sick himself and possibly even die. They all firmly believe in it, even the semi-educated ones. Well, in this instance the husband's doubts were realised and the woman *was* unfaithful. The Don Juan concerned is a native I know quite well; he runs a little store in the reserve. Shortly after his *affaire* he became sick. He complained of pains in his legs and back which grew progressively worse till he could hardly walk, and he became incredibly thin. He was taken to the clinic and the G.M.O., Dr Brodie, gave him a thorough check up, specimens taken, blood slides, everything. Brodie said he could find nothing wrong with him whatever. So the fellow went back to sit in his hut and nurse himself. He's still there, can hardly move and is appallingly thin. The only person who can cure him is an African doctor, but for some reason he won't consult one. And when I say the only person who can cure him, I really mean it. Had he *not* known that the woman had taken the medicine, I'm quite sure he'd be as healthy as ever, but he *did* know. And, in any case, there'd always be a suspicion in his mind that she *may* have taken the stuff. His ailment is purely due to auto-suggestion. You see, his fear of the stuff she took convinces him of its power and that in itself is sufficient to make him sick. In such circumstances he has no faith in Brodie because he knows that a European doctor would be acting in the dark. But if an *African* doctor gave him a medicine to combat the other, his faith in it would effect the cure because his mind would accept its potency. The strength of this ignorant fear is all too apparent in his otherwise unaccountable decline."

"I must tell Irma," said Belinda; "she says they haven't *got* any minds and are unable to think at all. But the medicine the woman took—what is it actually, or don't you know?"

"In my opinion it could have been Chamberlain's Cough Remedy and the result would be the same. The Africans tell one that it's a mixture of the bark of certain trees, the head and organs of certain fish and the brains of a crocodile. In other words the ingredients are not easily come by—if they were any Tom, Dick or Harry of a native could make the stuff himself and do the African doctor out of business. The maddening thing is that the explanation of the power of the mind, which is so obvious to us, to the African is inexplicable. So they remain firmly convinced of the Black Arts. An African medicine made him sick, an African medicine will make him well—useless to argue. And another thing. They have to *pay* their own African doctors, and pay them well. The medical aid they receive from us at the clinics is *free*; and it's a peculiarity of human nature to feel that what one pays for has more value than what one is given."

"Fancy!" mused Belinda. "The power of the mind. . . .

I suppose it's like the way Irma always gets one of her awful migraines when John wants to spend the day at the Ruwalo Club watching cricket—I mean she's *afraid* the cricket will give her a migraine so she *gets* the migraine before they go, and so they *don't* go and then it goes—I mean the *migraine* goes. I mean—well, the power of the mind—that's a sort of illustration."

"A most illuminating one!" drawled Derek.

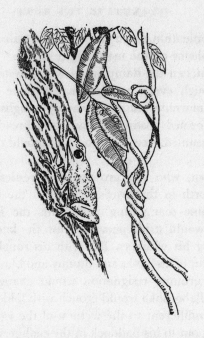

## CHAPTER NINE

IN February the sky became a massive sponge, restlessly elevated at times, stretching into near transparency, then shrinking, descending, expelling convulsive torrents of rain that swept in grey veils across the saturated earth. Weeds flourished in rank profusion and grass grew shoulder-high. Birds shook their limp feathers under the soggy leaves. Millipedes trailed their phantom footprints through the mud. Cockroaches multiplied. And throughout the humid nights mosquitoes sang their fiendish song.

Our ancient dwelling suffered. Mildew spread up the veranda walls in an ever-expanding bruise. Doors swelled in the moist air, opening and closing with the slow reluctance of rheumatic-ridden limbs. A drip above the fireplace followed the path of its predecessor with fatalistic monotony, gaining momentum down the irregular wall till it fell with suicidal violence on the mantelpiece below.

In the kitchen the damp wood was slow to burn. Smoke oozed through every opening in the stove and Langton made our morning tea with wheezy coughs and watering eyes. Salt formed obstinate lumps, and bread that was not rapidly consumed grew a reproachful mould on its softening crust.

Baboushka, who was growing into restless adolescence, ventured forth in the brief spells when the rain withheld, only to come scampering back with the first spattering drops. He would stride peevishly into the kitchen, sneezing and shaking his whiskers. But with his rough pink tongue raking the fur of his flanks and tummy and blue eyes dreamily narrowed, grumpy resignation would change to contentment, and Baboushka would crouch with folded paws beside the stove, indifferent to the wetness of the world outside.

Stepping out to his paddock in the cool grey monochrome of the morning, when the ground mist hung in static scarves between the trees and his wet fetlocks parted the long grass that lay prostrate with the weight of the night's rain, Dick Turpin tossed his head and whinnied. His velvet nostrils widened, inhaling the pungent fragrance of wet earth. His warm sepia eyes glowed. He executed a few prancing side-steps like some elderly dignitary skipping to the tune of irresistible music in the privacy of his bedroom.

That day he was released from the vegetative order of his semi-retirement. Together we wandered through the dripping trees and caught the elusive sweetness of rain-washed foliage. As though too shy to violate the water-muffled silence, red-eyed turtle doves sat in mute pairs on the branches above us, pressing their shoulders against each other in quiet understanding. Even the fallen nut-brown leaves of the *mahobohobo*—the wild loquat tree—that had crackled explosively underfoot now sank flabbily, soundlessly, into the soil beneath Dick Turpin's hooves. But the green-bellied parrots mocked the stillness, diving through the faint drizzle with raucous conversational shrieks and scarcely a wing-beat to maintain their rocket-swift propulsion; and minikin tree frogs that clung with spatulate toes to the wet bark sang in their piercing, two-toned trill—a song of trembling water drops and cold, green tree-light.

Guinea fowl were active. A flock of about thirty scratched sporadically for ants, calling with their staccato "kok-kok-kok-kerrrr kok-kok-kok". From a distance, scuttling with womanish uncertainty from one place to another, they resembled the fat grey beads of a broken necklace, rolling in all directions. Upon our approach they converged with startled *koks*, and the beads of the necklace were restrung as they tucked down their heads and ran between the drooping grass in single file—a rapid, silent retreat.

Presently I became aware of a persistent whisper, a prolonged sigh, swelling from the misted valley below us. As we descended, the sound thickened, acquired inflections, and rose and fell with the cadence of the sea. The river was in flood. When we reached its banks, the whispering had mounted to the hissing roar of escaping steam over full-throated bellows of thunder. The diffident tributary of the mighty mother Zambesi had risen in rebellion, revolting against its modest confines, sweeping beyond them with an imperious force that ignored unyielding obstacles and carried all others in the tumultuous, destructive power of its rolling arms. The fuscous water shot by with sinuous inter-fusions of rust-red, olive and milky brown, eddying and frothing in the furrowed banks and striking tree trunks with headlong force and showers of steely spray. Reeds bent horizontal and bobbed like desperate swimmers unable to advance. Saplings were caught by the ankles and shaken with brutal violence. Cumbersome logs were pried from their lichened repose and sent to join their hoary brethren which tossed and circled insanely below them. The lesser plunder of sticks and uprooted plants, drowned mice and leaves and writhing water weeds, swirling and jostling together, was carried till their drunken dance became irksome, when they were flung petulantly into the swaying fingers of the branches overhead, or hurled disdainfully among the far-thrown scum beyond the banks.

With a sudden sickening jolt I discerned something dark and round being buffeted downstream—the top of a pic-canin's head? Small and helpless it rose and sank and rose again while I watched in fascinated horror. With a devilish gurgle the water spun it closer and it somersaulted, erecting a withered stem . . . it was a native calabash. Sun-browned, dried and emptied of pulp and seed, it floated with obstinate buoyancy; independent, yet still oddly retaining the dead life I had unwillingly given it, the gourd paused an instant as if to leer at me before continuing on its hectic course.

Jennifer crossed the muddy parade ground to see me that afternoon with particles of raindrops gleaming silver on her eyebrows. My tale of a flooded river and a calabash head was overshadowed by news of far greater importance. "Dzokuti," she said, "is soon to have the honour of meeting a peer of the realm. I was up at the store this morning and Betty Harker couldn't contain herself. To give you the whole story from the beginning in more or less her own words, she was having a grand clean out of her pantry cupboard and, while thriftily wrapping a handful of broken candles in a sheet of newspaper torn from a week-old copy of the *Herald*, she happened to glance at the print. A name suddenly 'leapt out of the page at her!' In a small article it was reported that Lord Greaves was in the Federation on a visit to his aged aunt, the Hon. Mrs Howarth. I must say Betty was rather vague as to how and when she met Lord Greaves, but apparently she had known him well enough to feel that it would be *so* nice to renew the old ties of friendship. So she tracked down the Hon. Mrs Howarth, who lives in Salisbury, and sent a letter there addressed to Lord Greaves. She suggested that he might enjoy seeing a different part of the country and said that, if he could spare the time, she would *love* to have him for a weekend, a week, or even a month. I imagine she must have had to jog the old boy's memory as to just who she was. Anyway, she either painted an amazingly attractive picture of Dzokuti or the Hon. Mrs Howarth must be incredibly dull, because he has actually accepted! She even showed me his reply. As far as I can remember, it went something like 'I was charmed by the warmth of your kind invitation, though I must confess I was surprised that you should remember me so well, as our contact in England was a very fleeting one. I should be delighted to visit the wild and remote district in which you live. Unfortunately I have other commitments and cannot spare more than a day.' Then he goes on about how kind it is of her to offer to meet him and drive him down, and so on. Betty tried to sound blasé but she's in a turmoil and I think she's astonished that he accepted. She's getting Basil to repaint the lounge. Do you think she would if he was just *Mr* Greaves? Anyway, I shouldn't be catty, because she's very generously allowing us *all* to meet the peer. She's going to arrange a cocktail party and said she'd be sure to circulate the guests so that we could each have a few words with him in turn. I can't wait. And to think that only last Sunday Betty descended on us and Billy and I crawled down the passage on our hands and knees so that she couldn't see us pass the window! It worked, though; she only knocked for about five minutes before she gave up and left."

Though we all spoke of "Betty Harker's peer" with
derision, no one in Dzokuti was sufficiently indifferent to
refuse an invitation to her cocktail party. Letters of invitation were delivered by a piccanin some days later. Pierre
received ours in his office and it seemed to give him some
amusement for when he sent it across to me it was decorated
with scrolls and doodles in red ink for which Mrs Harker
could not have been responsible. Certain passages were also
marked with Pierre's pen in twirling red ink lines—"*Such an
opportunity . . . very well known in England . . . don't be shy . . . a
very unassuming man*".

But though we all accepted with one accord, our motives
for doing so appeared to differ.

"I'm perfectly certain his title's phoney," said Brenda
Fawcett, flicking her cigarette ash and smiling with cool
indulgence at Belinda's unconcealed awe. "At all events,
Michael and I will definitely go, if only for the fun of prick-
ing the balloon, so to speak."

"Well, we get little enough variety here," said Jennifer.
"I think the whole thing's going to be great fun, whether
you prick a balloon or not—rather as though he was some
rare animal Betty had caught and we can all go and stare
at it before it gets away!"

With hands on her hips, Irma Dutoit sniffed: "I've always
said to John that titles are two a penny in England today
and why should a titled man be any different from anyone
else? Just downright snobbishness, I say. These titled gentlemen always think they're the bee's knees—so patronising
to ordinary people like us that you'd think we were factory
workers or something. I'm going to take John just to *show*
him what I mean. And if this lord's stuck up, I'm going to
get up and walk out—just like that!"

Derek stroked his nose and smiled maliciously. "Without
intending blasphemy, I feel this will go down in the annals

of Dzokuti's history as the 'Day the Lord Came'. I simply couldn't resist such a delightful prospect. One imagines us all trooping in like a crowd of shuffling villagers, touching our caps and mumbling a welcome. Of course, the chief enjoyment will be derived from the flurries and twitterings of our triumphant hostess."

It was generally known that the Fanshawes had received and accepted an invitation and we wondered if they, too, had been told that Lord Greaves was a very unassuming man of whom they must not be shy. It was also rumoured that an invitation had been extended to Oliver Lindsay, for Mrs Harker had remarked that "bachelors working on tobacco farms lead such an isolated, lonely life, that I feel we should include them in our little social activities as often as possible". Of the many bachelors who fell into this category Oliver Lindsay was the only one to benefit from Mrs Harker's kindliness. Perhaps it was felt that the other young men would not enjoy these social activities, disfigured as they were with short, plump legs, uncouth accents, prominent Adam's apples, or sharp elbows and pimples.

Being aware that a preview of the distinguished guest might have gratified our curiosity and thereby lessened the attraction of the evening's entertainment, Betty Harker kept Lord Greaves in close confinement throughout the day of his visit. If he was driven through the wild, wet hills to appreciate their qualities of remoteness and untamed beauty, the tour had been conducted along little-used tracks and the vicinity of Dzokuti had been avoided.

When stars flickered out with a chill brilliance between the dim clouds, the warmer beam of a car's headlights penetrated the shadows of the Fanshawes' drive, defined the gate pillars, and glowed down the dark road beyond.

A tactful message from an unknown source had been

circulated among us intimating that an arrival *en masse*
would be a little overwhelming and introductions consequently hurried, confused and ineffectual.

When the red tail-light of the Fanshawes' car had glim-
mered up the winding road and snuffed itself out between
the trees, Jennifer and Billy Burkitt therefore allowed some
minutes to elapse before their own departure. It was
arranged that the Fawcetts should follow, but Michael drove
down to us at a speed that scattered the gravel in all directions and told us to precede them, as Brenda was having
trouble with her hair and would be delayed a few minutes
longer.

As Pierre and I mounted the steps beneath the sagging
bougainvillea, the generous outline of Betty Harker appeared in the light of the open doorway, inclined at an
inquiring angle on her pylon-heeled shoes. She motioned us
into the room with a graciously extended arm.

Jennifer, Billy and Mrs Fanshawe were grouped in a
corner, commenting upon the savouries which they nibbled
with that unnatural enthusiasm which so often reassures the
doubting hostess. Lord Greaves stood with his back to the
fireplace. He was tall and stooped. His hair was silvery
white, his face creased with benign lines, and his faded blue
eyes dreamy and unseeing, as though he were drifting away
from present company. At the moment of our entry his
attention was held by Mr Fanshawe, who thwarted Mrs
Harker in her attempts at an introduction for several
minutes by manœuvring his unconscious back between
ourselves and Lord Greaves.

"The racial problem is something this country must face
squarely," Mr Fanshawe was saying, "no doubt about it.
But it is a problem which can be resolved. Without fear of
contradiction I may say the whole thing is merely a question

of seeing things in perspective. I mean the situation must be viewed as a whole, not as a series of small, unrelated incidents. We must look at things in proportion. What I mean to say is, we must see things on a broader plane."

"I see. And what do you feel would be the best policy?" said Lord Greaves, who had not yet seen us. Mr Fanshawe rocked on his heels and blew out his cheeks. "Well . . . er, well we must have a *far-sighted* policy." He was spared from enlarging upon this sound assertion, for Mrs Harker attracted Lord Greaves with an apologetic cough, and we were introduced.

"Pierre is our constable," Mrs Harker explained, lowering her voice to the tone of one who discloses a circumstance both dangerous and rare—a tone which might have been more commensurable with the revelation that Pierre was in the Secret Service.

"The B.S.A. Police have a very fine reputation," remarked Lord Greaves. But while Pierre was left to discuss the merits of the police force with the principal guest, I was firmly drawn aside and conducted by my hostess to a plate of cheese *aigrettes*. My turn had not yet come.

"Now *do* help yourself!" she cried. "Don't wait to be asked. I've sent Basil to get two more tins of sardines out of the store for the cook to prepare . . . just in case."

Mrs Fanshawe and I were telling each other for the second time that the cheese *aigrettes* were excellent when Brenda and Michael made their entrance. Brenda approached Lord Greaves with an outstretched hand and an encouraging smile.

"I've heard *so* much about you!" She spoke with an air of expectancy, as though hoping to confound him with this emphatic utterance. When he raised a questioning eyebrow, she turned to Betty Harker with a faintly bitter and vaguely incriminatory smile, murmuring; "Betty dear,

I'm simply pining for a whisky. I thought Michael would *never* be ready this evening—so dithery!"

Michael accepted this traitorous charge with impunity. No more regard was paid to our host's uncertain reappearance than had been given to his prolonged absence. "C-c-couldn't find the sardines. Gave the c-cook some tins of fish paste . . .'—Mr Harker addressed himself to the unresponsive carpet. Car doors slammed outside and hurrying forward to receive the latest arrivals Mrs Harker brushed a streak of dust from her husband's sleeve with an absent-minded frown as though he were an unoccupied suit suspended from a coat-hanger.

Irma Dutoit walked vigorously into our circle of indefinite laughs and half-finished sentences. Her sister followed with less resolution, and her husband with obvious reluctance. On being presented to Lord Greaves, Mrs Dutoit's expression was one of strong suspicion, but she nevertheless said that she was pleased to meet him. Having done so, she retreated with her back to the wall, and lips compressed, obediently followed by her husband and Belinda. But the latter had been calmed by a friendly smile from Lord Greaves and was able to show more interest in the varieties of snacks and savouries waiting on the table beside her.

To be seen at a cocktail party with neither drink, canapé nor cigarette, standing with empty hanging hands, produces the same feeling of acute discomfort as one might experience if one attempted to paddle in the foaming lip of a wave wearing high heels, a tight dress and furs, while more suitably unclad bathers romped around one with curious stares. One is awkward, conspicuous and helpless, as though one went into battle unarmed. Our little discussions were accordingly restless and disjointed until we were all agreeably settled with these necessities. We were, in fact, pressed to take two snacks at a time by our anxious hostess, with a resulting contortion of our fingers and scattering of crumbs. But once the conflicting flavours of smoke, sherry and mashed sardines humoured our palates, the fidgeting ceased; sagacity and poise returned.

" I do hope dear Oliver will be able to come," said Betty Harker. "I hear the river's still very high and of course he has to cross it to reach us. I remember how it washed away great chunks of concrete from that bridge when it flooded last year." She smiled at Lord Greaves, "Of course I must enlighten you, mustn't I? Oliver Lindsay is going to become one of our rich tobacco barons one day!"

"Oh, really? Inheriting an estate, is he?"

"Oh no, no! Nothing like that. He's starting the hard way as assistant on a tobacco farm. He'll be . . . how do they say it in the Navy? Coming up from the bilge hole . . . or is it through a hawse pipe? Such a delightful young man! So many young men today seem to bear a grudge against life. And they're so clumsy in speech and manner and their conversation only becomes really lively when it concerns *cars*. They're completely at a loss in feminine society! With our Oliver it's quite the reverse. Full of wit and charm and gaiety. He has a certain masculine grace. What I would call a *valiant* boy. A real Sir Lancelot . . . or was it Galahad?"

" I have an idea it was Sir Lancelot," cried a voice from the dark veranda, and Oliver Lindsay, with well-brushed hair and a spotted bow tie, stepped smiling into the room, causing Mrs Harker to squeak and splash a little whisky on her shoe. Brenda Fawcett fingered her pearl necklace and became absorbed in a bowl of nasturtiums. Belinda, who had been hovering undecided over a gherkin and a stuffed egg, lifted the egg with tremulous haste and turned to her sister with an incomprehensible burst of laughter.

"And who," said Oliver with a wistfully upraised eyebrow, "will be my Guinevere? Or Elaine, my lily maid of Astolat? Or, better still, my doomed Lady of Shalott?" The posing of this romantic problem allowed Betty Harker to regain her self-possession.

" Lord Greaves, let me introduce the young man we've been speaking about!" She wagged her finger at Oliver, "Naughty boy! Don't you know eavesdroppers always hear ill of themselves?"

" Then this must have been the exception that proves the rule," said Oliver with a complacent chuckle.

Derek Vaughn arrived a moment later with a languid apology for his tardiness. "I am possessed by a family of cats," he drawled, "and one of its younger and more obnoxious members succeeded in scaling the drainpipe to the roof. Having reached that sublime height, he found himself quite unable to descend. Rescuing him was a lengthy business, and not without risk."

Though Derek was given a cordial reception, his presence did not excite the same agitation which Oliver's appearance had aroused. Also it was evident to the most casual and indifferent observer that between Derek and Oliver there existed a certain degree of antipathy. Their mutual aversion revealed itself in their almost unmannerly attempts to surpass each other in anecdote and cynicism, and in their unsuccessful endeavours to engage Lord Greaves in a discussion from which the other could be excluded. Derek had no sooner dwelt upon the possible significance of the African National Congress on the country's future, when Oliver entertained Lord Greaves with a detailed account of the curing and grading of tobacco.

Mrs Harker found it no longer necessary to circulate her guests, who had of their own accord formed a polite semi-circle about the declamatory bachelors. During one of the pauses, when Betty Harker urged her husband to replenish our glasses and pass the sausage rolls, Oliver asked Lord Greaves what his impressions were of "this degenerate little corner of the Empire". Lord Greaves hesitated, and the vestige of a smile deepened the lines on either side of his mouth. "The word degenerate," he said, "implies a sad decline from a former excellence. I don't really think Rhodesia could be described as going downhill. Rather to the contrary. But if I were to conform to the rules I suppose I should first be expected to remark upon the glorious sub-tropical climate. So I break rule number one. Weather's atrocious. Been raining ever since I arrived. The next conventional statement deals of course with the racial question. The White Settlers and the Blacks, as they say in our papers at home. I break rule number two. Won't even venture an opinion on the thing. Sick of it. Then the approved traveller talks impressively of the *big game*. I'm far too stiff in the joints to risk a safari. Although I'm an ardent nature-lover, I'm afraid I must even break rule number three. The only wild life I have so far observed is a tortoise. At least, I *thought* it was a tortoise, but Mrs Harker rather dashed my hopes by saying it was merely a stone. I was only afforded a brief glimpse of it as we passed and was unable to make notes on its habits." His eyes gleamed with amusement:

" How very fortunate it is that when I return to England I shall not be called upon to address any societies or gatherings on the subject of my expedition to Africa!"

Irma Dutoit pursed her lips and nodded. "I've always told my husband that Africa's a very much overrated country," she said with satisfaction. Lord Greaves looked thoughtful and when he spoke again his voice was gentle, deliberate and slow. "I don't agree with you at all," he said. "Though I've only been here a week, I have in fact fallen in love with the country. There's a sort of tremendous, sleepy grandeur about it. I think most visitors would become conscious of that. I don't really think any other country has it. . . . The feeling of dormant power is very much a part of Africa."

Oliver had been the first to put a question to Lord Greaves and in doing so he released the more timid guests from their hitherto deferential silence. The titled visitor became the focal point of the diversified queries that followed. Belinda boldly asked him if he had been to the Victoria Falls and, on learning that he had not, John Dutoit displayed a greater originality in asking if he had seen the Zimbabwe Ruins. After that it was considered that the subject of Rhodesia had been fully dealt with and Betty Harker asked if he had perhaps been present at the coronation. "How well I remember seeing it on the screen in Salisbury!" she said. "All the wonderful pageantry and glitter! The robes and diamonds! The deafening crowds . . . and the stately peers in their coronets! It was all so splendid!"

"Very c-c-colourful," murmured Mr Harker.

"It was indeed," said Lord Greaves, "but I certainly did not take part in it. Good heavens, no! I viewed the ceremony on the television set from the comfortable depths of my armchair."

"Do you go up to the House often?" asked Brenda Fawcett, with a knowledgeable tilt to her head.

"Haven't done so for years. Never cared for controversy. I live in the country, you know, and I'm one of those contented old souls who prefer to sit fishing by a tranquil stream . . . thinking of nothing at all."

Conscious that Lord Greaves was not conforming to pattern, and that some of her guests had come in expectation of meeting a more illustrious figure, Betty Harker sought to colour the drab effect which she felt he had produced.

"Of course," she said, "how right you are to watch the world go by from the grounds of your lovely old home. The terraced lawns and wooded parks, the leaping salmon, the antlered stag, and the . . . the grouse! There's simply no substitute for such magnificent surroundings. And when one thinks of all the glory and history that lies behind it!" Lord Greaves smiled, but remained silent.

"To me the very idea of a peerage lasting only for one life's duration is shocking!" she continued. "To abolish hereditary titles is to abolish all the noble tradition that goes with them. I feel it would be the end of the English saga!"

"I suppose it depends on how old the title is," said Irma Dutoit with a tinge of acrimony in her voice. "You do get these rich Jews and people with the title only going back one generation. Often they *bought* them, didn't they, John?"

Mr Dutoit, who had but a moment since placed an entire chicken patty in his mouth, acquired a heightened colour and was unable to reply.

The subject of hereditary titles led inevitably to a dissertation on the knighthoods conferred upon sportsmen in recent years—a matter upon which everyone had something to say, with the exception of Lord Greaves, who withdrew from the debate with a dreamy smile.

Mr Fanshawe plunged into the fray with portentous enthusiasm, Michael Fawcett with delicate irony, and Mrs Harker with a sweeping vehemence. Jennifer Burkitt expressed herself with ribald humour, and Mrs Fanshawe with humourless tact.

Both Brenda Fawcett and Oliver retired from the wrangle at an early stage and, drawing aside, entered into a mild and scarcely audible flirtation, Brenda accepting Oliver's bland compliments with every appearance of delight, de-pite the sarcasm with which she parried his attentions. Belinda was unaware of this interesting dalliance until the whispering of some more extravagant tribute caused Brenda to throw back her head with a silvery laugh and say "How sweet!" Then Belinda sagged visibly. Her shoulders twitched no longer with sprightly shrugs, her head no longer tossed, her hands ceased to flutter and with a forlorn smile she refused a proffered roll of smoked ham, the last on the plate.

Diverted in turn by this distressing little drama and by the still unsettled dispute as to whether Tom Bounceball, the golf champion, deserved to become Sir Thomas Bounceball, I was startled when the clock on the mantelpiece cleared its throat with an introductory whirring and groaning and proclaimed the hour to the tune of a nursery jingle.

"Good gracious me!" cried Betty Harker, "ten o'clock! And we promised Lady . . . Mrs Howarth to have you back in Salisbury before midnight, Lord Greaves! I fear we must bring our party to an end! *Oh*, and my poor little Porky-pie has been locked up in my bedroom all this time! How *could* his mumsy be so cruel!"

The ring of disaster in her voice penetrated the consciousness of even the most preoccupied guest, and handbags, wraps and cigarette cases were gathered in haste as though a crisis were impending. Billy Burkitt forgetting himself so far as to mutter "Crikey!"

But Mrs Harker brought us to order again by thanking Lord Greaves, on behalf of us all, for his kindness in visiting our isolated little community and brightening, if only for an evening, the dull routine of our lives.

## CHAPTER TEN

VISITS to Salisbury were rare. The prospect of such an event filled us with delight and produced a flutter of activity. The financing of the expedition was, of course, the primary question—one that Pierre and I tossed lightly back and forth over the breakfast table, treated with serious and somewhat depressing deliberation over lunch, and discussed with heavy pessimism sprinkled with a few sharp disagreements over dinner. Finally, alternating between "Let's enjoy ourselves", and "We must be realistic", we resolved the impasse with compromise and proposed retrenchments.

Shopping lists were compiled. They began with such items as ink, new dish-cloths, and khaki darning wool. Then a brighter note would creep in—"earrings to go with the yellow cotton frock", and "one yard nylon lace" would appear. The wild, wicked extravagance displayed at the end of the list with "half pound of salami" and "blue-green eye-shadow" was to some extent subdued by the tentative question marks that preceded these suggestions.

Next, the preparations were made: cupboards locked and keys hidden; contradictory orders given to the cook; and a basin placed on the mantelpiece to catch the drip if it should rain.

Having washed the windows and dusted the seats of the car with mournful diligence, Langton made his presence known in the living-room by giggling weakly in the doorway and rubbing his chin.

"What is it?" said Pierre.

"Mambo, is one year las' time I'm going to see Sosbry. Now I'm want to going see Sosbry this time. Las' time I'm going in bus. Better this time I'm going in motor-carie with Mambo for see Sosbry?"

"What do you want to do in Salisbury?" asked Pierre. Langton scratched his head reflectively and sighed, "Eh-h, plenty too much!"

We left Dzokuti the following morning before sunrise. The new day stretched its arms in the dew, and the *Flappet* lark threw itself up into the pale green sky, rattling its wings together like a pair of joyous castanets. When the sun seeped higher over the rim of the smoke-coloured hills the *msasa* trees spread their lacy shadows across the damp sand of the road as though gently discarding the cloaks of sleep.

Langton shifted on the back seat and yawned. In his town attire he had altered beyond recognition. His head had been fashionably shaved the previous evening and bore the like-ness of a large though unsymmetrical chocolate Easter egg. He wore a navy-blue, pin-striped suit and a pair of black

shoes that gaped at his instep. His bleary eyes were framed
in spectacles. Empty frames, for the glass had been deemed
unnecessary and removed; but the frames themselves lent
the final touch of sophistication to a transformed cook boy.
For the present, however, his simplicity of manner was un-
changed. He slipped lower on the car seat and, when he
could slide no farther, abandoned himself to sleep.

The sun mounted, chasing nocturnal creatures to their
burrows, giving leaves a tinsel nimbus, drying the drenched
grass, and scintillating on the windscreen of the car. The
far lavender range of hills darkened to a multitude of greens
until we passed, then sank dreamily behind us, their granite
contours smoothed again to a dim blue silhouette. Within
their tranquil folds lay an insect-humming solitude. Before
us . . . the tarmac and the toil of mankind.

Langton jerked awake at the swish of a passing car and
sat forward. "Plenty too fast, Mambo!" he muttered
hoarsely, as fence posts and telegraph poles floated by.
Pierre turned to address me as we approached a small
bridge, and Langton breathed hard down the back of
Pierre's neck: "You got *bridge* come, Mambo!" he shouted,
his bulging eyes imploring Pierre to concentrate on the road
ahead. The remaining miles to Salisbury brought increasing
strain to Langton's nerves. If sunlight flashed on the roof of
a car a quarter of a mile away and Pierre forgot himself
sufficiently to glance at the passing scenery, Langton
brought him back firmly to the matter in hand: "You got
*cars* come, Mambo!"

When we reached the suburbs, however, he allowed himself to relax. We drove slowly down the wide avenues that
were so green and cool with the dappled shadows of jacaran-
das and flame trees by day, and so sombre after dark, when
pedestrians hurried through the dim, uneasy light, and had

cause to grumble at the dearth of street lamps. The towering blocks of flats, the gleaming rows of cars, the aeroplanes that droned overhead—to Langton all these were of no consequence and were dismissed. Twisting on his seat and pressing his face to the window, he followed the movements of the gaily whistling African delivery boys that bicycled by, and the smartly-clad African women whose high heels tapped along the pavements.

We conveyed our cook to the busiest and noisiest section of the city, where a maze of street intersections is partially rectified by a corresponding maze of islands. The kerbs of the islands are faced with black and white paving and the resulting confusion of chequered loops and deviations bears such a marked resemblance to bovine intestines that Salisbury dwellers have given the area the apt if indelicate title of Cow's Guts. Frustrated drivers hoot in vain while pedestrians pause to gossip; Africans sit on the kerbs and sing; coloured and Indian children race giddily through the crowds; alley cats prowl; mongrels fight; bicycle bells jangle; people argue. A medley of hot jazz tunes competes from the doors of every Indian bazaar, and the shop windows tempt the shuffling onlookers with gaudy displays and giant posters in scarlet letters proclaiming "Bargain Sales" and "Greatly Reduced Prices". The air is heavy with the odour of petrol fumes and cheap tobacco, fish and chips, coffee, spices, stale buns and perspiration.

A conspicuous corner was chosen for our reunion with Langton at the end of the day. We told him to be there at sunset and warned him not to stray if we chanced to be late. Langton assured us he would be there without fail. He left us with a smile of dazed wonderment, and was instantly caught up in the swirling throng and lost to view.

To wait for an indefinite length of time on a street corner when dusk falls drably over the city would give no pleasure to a European. He would stand, shifting his weight from one tired foot to the other. Self-conscious, he would gaze ahead with haughty vacancy, feeling and ignoring the curious glances of every passer-by—impertinent people. He would consult his watch without registering the hour, and one minute later consult his watch again. He would sigh, frown, tap his foot, take a few fretful steps along the pavement, retrace them to the corner, and stand there once more, gazing scornfully down the street.

In similar circumstances Langton would have no such inhibitions, and in his freedom suffer no boredom. He would sit on the kerb with his large shoes in the gutter and his back against a lamp-post. Having no horror of strangers, he would hail his fellow Africans and many would linger to establish a fleeting friendship. Viewed from behind, the retreating figure of a fat African matron could provide no better subject for unsubtle jokes and shared guffaws. With his determination to find entertainment he would have a colourful section of life about him to laugh at, to shout at, to puzzle over, to enjoy. With his unselfconscious delight why should he not raise his toneless voice and sing? Why not whistle through his teeth? Why not stare? Why not talk to that strange boy on a bicycle about his new shirt and, as he pedalled down the street, shout all the louder till distance carried his voice no farther? Why not unwrap his little newspaper parcel on the pavement and tear at the loaf of bread and drain the bottle of lemonade it contained? Why not drag his jacket over his head when he was tired of it all and have a short snooze? Why not?

From the Cow's Guts Pierre and I drove to Salisbury's shopping centre. We circled the blocks with a desperate eye for a parking space and, some ten minutes later, found one. Several months in Dzokuti had produced in me a not yet rooted calm that was severely shaken by its first readjustment to the small bustle of Stanley Avenue. I felt a certain rustic apprehension towards traffic.

Jostled by large women and tripping over their unpredictable children we inspected shop windows with the same sedulous attention which Langton was no doubt exhibiting as he was carried forward by the surging throng in the Cow's Guts. But here we found no greatly reduced prices, for such a shameless admittance would draw the wrong customer. A pair of Italian shoes balanced their tapered toes on a shell-pink pedestal and attracted an admiring press of onlookers. Their steel-rod heels wore a descending spiral of crystal beads that would toss and tinkle as the proud wearer revolved on her precarious spikes. A modest card below them bore the price, forty guineas, without as much as hinting at a bargain. We passed on to windows where stockings wove a multi-shaded cobweb of studied negligence; to festoons of material that shimmered like a fountain in the sun or glowed like water lapping in the moonlight. Their colours were identified for the ignorant: peridot and avocado, vanilla, tobacco, pink mica and nectarine.

Salisbury is a pleasing town. The air is as yet unpolluted by industrial dust and the sunlight unimpeded by a plethora of architectural wedding cakes. The streets are attractively wide, so planned in the early days to facilitate the turning of spanned oxen. A few early buildings still remain; two-storied and tin-roofed, sandwiched between the austere heights of modern erections and giving the impression of graceless, faded flowers pressed with sentimental incongruity between the pages of a contemporary novel, but they are being demolished. Superior structures rise in succession. Neon signs replace the painted signs of swinging tin. Old Salisbury inhabitants halt in confusion when chill labels pasted on empty windows inform them that their favourite dress- or sweet-shop will be moving to new premises. A week later the old building will be a heap of rubble, with the shouts of labourers, the squeaking of pulley ropes, the grind of concrete mixers and the roar of the bulldozers that nose the yielding earth into new foundations. Girders and scaffolding pattern the skyline. Pavements are removed overnight, substituted by wooden platforms, with corrugated iron shelters overhead to protect the unwary pedestrian from showers of dust and falling bricks. And the pedestrian is compelled to skirt round sudden excavations and to approach blind alleys with caution for fear of the truck, loaded with sand and cement, that may emerge.

We walked the length of First Street with aimless deliberation. New Rhodesians filled the town. Continentals chattered in their mother tongue. Bold-eyed Italian men sauntered by, some of them perhaps workers on the great Kariba Dam project, spending their holiday in customary idleness. In the shops, assistants spoke with a soft Irish or a twangy Lancashire accent. Teen-aged girls with fringes and pony-tails and circular skirts loitered beside the cinema houses of First Street. Youths who revelled in their title of "First Street Cowboys" roared past on motor-bikes; they showed a preference for jeans and leather lumber-jackets, the backs of which ballooned in the wind and were painted with such obscure slogans as "Rock your Doll" and "The Be-bop Bugs". But if this hopeful rising generation appeared to be cast in a mould that was neither inimitable nor unique, they were not perverted, hardened sinners; I saw no sign of addiction to drugs. They sucked chocolates and pepper-mints and stared placidly at grotesquely enlarged posters of Rock Hudson and Debbie Reynolds.

One well-patronised store had bills pasted on its windows from which we learnt that Madame Frachot, the representative of a French firm of cosmetiques, was at that very moment awaiting us at their cosmetic department, ready with free advice on all our skin and make-up problems. Such an offer could not be rejected.

Mme. Frachot sat at one end of the counter, distinguished by a silver-lettered placard which bore her name. She met our eyes and smiled eagerly. Pierre muttered. The black marocain that enfolded her bosom was dusted with powder. She had hooded eyelids and a gold-filled front tooth. Her mauve lips and buff complexion were shadowed by a black gauze hat that held a full-blown magenta rose in the provocative droop of its brim. She stood, and we could no longer retreat. Her expression was inquiring, solicitous, speculative and faintly critical. She interrupted my vague comment upon the variety of bottles and jars with which she was surrounded.

"Per-raps you know of our products? They are famous throughout France. . . ." I was forced to admit that I had never heard of them.

"No? But in France they are the choice of the multifold! Regular application of our crèmes will give *amazing* results. I myself, I use no other!" I dropped my eyes hurriedly from the pouched, buff cheeks and guiltily fingered a sample pot of foundation cream. Madame Frachot bent closer. "Such beautiful shades," she breathed. "For you let me suggest this *Orchide Tendre*? So young, and for you, Madame, so *right!*" She flashed her gold-filled tooth at Pierre with an air of conspiracy.

"Would you not have it so? Your wife is an orchid to be cherished from this most inconsiderate African sun. With our *crème nutricia* she will be for ever the *jeune fille*. I myself, I use this excellent crème always! For powder—none other than *Printemps!* And of course the *cosmétique pour les cils!* I would insist upon. . . ." Now or never, I decided, and, stepping back, trod on Pierre's toe. "I'm sorry," I said, "I'm afraid

I was really just having a look. Perhaps some other time when I'm not in a hurry. . . ." The cloying atmosphere of intimacy was at once dispelled and the gold tooth vanished. "But of course, Madame. Just as you please." She removed the sample pot of cream firmly from my unconscious fingers and looked distantly over my shoulder, seeking a more profitable client.

We moved on. I looked at my shopping list and read: Blue-green eye-shadow; Half-pound salami. But Madame Frachot had rather put me off both these items. Also Pierre began to look preoccupied and slightly bemused. He showed a faint response at the suggestion of tea.

Though there are a great many places where Salisbury shoppers may obtain respite to ease their legs and enjoy a cup of tea, Meikle's Hotel still draws the majority. A point of convergence for the gregarious, it is the inevitable meeting ground of farmers and families from country districts.

The hotel lounge when we entered contained a babble of voices that rose and fell above the despairing strains of the small orchestra. After we had secured a table the profusion of pale, blob-like faces emerged as personalities, turning to their neighbours, bowing to their tea-cups, stretching into smiles, munching cake. Sunburnt, jocular tobacco farmers —there were too, of course, sunburnt, solemn tobacco farmers; but being out of character they are not worth mentioning—immaculate continental businessmen smiling insincerely at their associates; a few Rhodesian businessmen, less immaculate; expensively dressed city women with curious hats; housewives with lumpish paper bags and aching feet. Viewed collectively, people are an amusing or a depressing spectacle, depending upon the temperament of the objective spectator.

The small number of women in Salisbury who are

G

entranced by their own appearance, and haunted by the self-imposed necessity of obeying to the last button the commands of fashion, are handicapped. Frustrated not only by unflattering lines and oddly rebellious fatty tissues, they are faced with a problem which their sisters in England and Europe never encounter: the suitability of the surroundings and the worthiness of the occasion. For them there are no Henleys, Ascots and Savoys at which their uneasily narrow or peculiarly bulbous silhouettes can appear. Nevertheless, the knowledge that they are an embodiment of the cataleptic visions in *Vogue* brings such a happy sparkle to their eyes that the inappropriateness of their garb for a morning's shopping and tea at Meikle's can be forgiven. They are as much a part of the entertainment as the members of the orchestra who play with fortitude above the din. The disdainful sway of their entry, the slow grace with which they draw off their long suède gloves, the poise with which they pour their tea, and their unerring if unconscious ability to display an ankle or profile give gratification no less to themselves than to their spectators.

They were only momentarily eclipsed by a group of hip-conscious models from Israel who glittered briefly in the centre of the lounge over their iced tomato juice before being shepherded off to the airport to continue their tour. And they were only fleetingly disturbed as cups were again arrested when an unheeding blonde passed slowly between the tables with parted lips and a distracted air, followed by sibilant whispers; "That's Miss Bulawayo—you know, the Beauty Queen!"

To balance the entertainment with more human interest there is the fat woman at the opposite table who has slipped off her worn shoes and, expelling her breath unconsciously, raises from her cream puff a little cloud of icing sugar which settles on her chin. She is absorbed in her favourite magazine.

Watching her lips move as she turns the pages one can almost divine the contents. The recipe page with "lightning-quick puddings for that Unexpected Guest"; the page with appeals to *Aunt Cathy, Your Friend and Adviser*: "My boyfriend has gone to work in another town. He never writes to me. What should I do?" Or: "My husband's mother lives with us, and as she accepts our hospitality I feel she should mind the kiddies sometimes when we want to go to the pictures. *Am I right in this?*" The pen-pal section: "Girl (18) would like pen-pals (men 18-25). Interests—Pat Boone, Doris Day and Presley records. Badminton. Collecting pictures of the Royal Family." The tense serial story about the exemplary nurse, Pamela Marston, who suppresses her love for the firm-lipped Dr Bradley, who in his turn is temporarily infatuated with the scheming, malicious model, Vanessa Black. And the short romance of the London typist who met Mr Right on her week's holiday at Clovelly. "He walked towards her over the pebbles on the beach, the seagulls cried overhead, and she knew the moment she saw him that none other could ever command her heart." He never lost his balance among the pebbles and the seagulls never dropped white stains on his stalwart shoulders.

At the other tables the perpetual shoppers were distinguished by the scarcity of parcels in their laps. They were the sort of women who bustle into town four days a week to match a card of buttons and buy a new kitchen strainer. Pierre remarked on the hats as they came and went.

"Good Lord, there goes a woman with an improbable garden trellis on her head!" And: "Here's one wearing a preposterous yellow *pot de chambre* with a bow for the handle." Defence of my own sex was weak.

We were interrupted from this engrossing study by a whoop behind us.

" Well, well, *well*; if it isn't old Pierre, the Perverted

Policeman!" We turned, as did several others, at this un-
desirable salutation, and found Bert Goldman's amiable
face creased in smiles.

"Knew I'd meet *some* Dzokuti type here!" he roared,
"I'll join you if I can only find a chair to sit myself on."
He looked about and discovered a vacant chair at an ad-
joining table. He beamed ingratiatingly at the sleek young
woman beside it, "Beg pardon, Miss, you wanting this chair?
No? Ta, I'll just heave it across, if you don't object."
He seated himself with a thud between us and yawned
loudly.

"Hell's bells, what a morning! Been chasing about town
trying to find spare parts for the tractors. The wife's at the
dentist, but I got a big thirst on an' I can't wait. What'll it
be? You drinking *tea*? Faugh! Move those cups over! This
one's on me. How's it for a beer? *Waiter!* Three beers,
*three*, an' make 'em *cold*." He settled back again with his
jolly, frog-like smile and rubbed his hands.

"You two been on the spree, hey? That's the ticket, give
it stick! Old Dolly gave it stick this morning—just about
cleaned me out buying herself a fancy dance dress for this
big dance they're getting up at the Ellis-Parkers'. Reckon
I'll have to wear dark glasses, there's so many sequins on
that dress!" Bert Goldman grew more loquacious with every
draught of beer. Straining at first to keep pace with his
rambling exuberance above the discordant hubbub of the
room, we found ourselves gradually shrinking into a state of
numbly smiling passivity. We were startled out of this
quiescence when he contemplated us for a moment over the
rim of his glass, then set it back on the table with force and
leant forward. "What're you folks doing tonight? How's
about us beating up the town together?"

Pierre answered with haste: "Er . . . thanks very much,
Bert, but we'd rather we got home reasonably early. It's

a long trip back, you know. Have to be up pretty early tomorrow—working day and all that."

Bert was not so easily dissuaded. "Ah, come off it! You're only young once. Couple of aspirin tomorrow and you'll be as right as rain. Come on now, Carol, tell that husband of yours to shake a leg. I tell you what—you two join up with the ol' lady an' me and we'll go to the Coq d'Or. How's that? Man, it's a wonderful place for celebrating. Don't you let those stuffed shirts you see there put you off. Call themselves the Government House crowd, *faugh*! Trouble with them is they're too ruddy stuck up. I'd like to see them come unstuck. I promise you it'll be a night to remember!"

"I've no doubt it will," said Pierre without spirit, "but we're not frightfully affluent just at present. Have to be fairly careful, you know."

"*Faugh!* Party's on me!"

Pierre looked uneasy and I ventured another rather lame excuse. "Bert, that's really very nice of you," I said, "but I simply can't go to the Coq d'Or in what I'm wearing, and I've nothing to change into."

"What's wrong with that, for Pete's sake? You just stay as sweet as you are, as they tell the kids over the radio on their birthday requests. We'll do it in style. Wine, women and song! Good old vino!" he kissed his finger tips and Pierre looked increasingly uncomfortable.

"Bert, old man, it's very decent of you, but the snag is I shan't be able to dance. My shoes you know, rubber soles." Pierre regarded this declaration as conclusive and sat back in some relief. Bert guffawed.

"All the better! You just swig the old vino and keep an eye on Dolly and I'll keep Carol jigging about the floor. Take 'em both on if you like. Oh, we'll make it a hectic night. A slap-up dinner. Ever tasted their trout fresh from Inyanga? Boy, will I make a pig of myself! Soft lights, sweet music . . . lovely creatures gliding about to the good old dance band throb. Last time we went they had a smooth dame with a violin. Wanders around between the tables playing, you know. She stopped at our table an' played the thing over us while we were eating. She stoops, you know, with a nice low dress on . . . umm! Long hair flopping over her face, an' big owl's eyes. I'd have pinched her bottom if Dolly hadn't been watching me. Good old vino. . . . No, I tell you what! Vodka, that's the thing. A little vodka down the old Gulf Stream an' there's no holding me. I tell you, there's just no holding me!" Bert attracted a good deal of attention, punctuating his remarks by striking the table with the palm of his hand which caused our glasses to quiver and the beer to lurch wildly within them. Convinced that every-one within hearing was regarding our table with amuse-ment or distaste, the delights which Bert prophesied only increased my discomfort. I clearly foresaw the ripple of innumerable raised eyebrows as Coq d'Or vino and vodka took its effect on the boisterous Bert Goldman. I had an unhappy vision of indignant couples leaving the dance floor as Bert led me whooping and rollicking among them. He voiced my fears.

"Know how to rumba? Good old dago dancing! *Caramba!* Just let me get those drums of theirs an' I'll beat you a rhythm'll send those band boys hopping about like cats on a burning roof!"

"Bert, it all sounds lovely," I said, "but I've just remem-bered: we're taking our cook boy back with us and we really can't keep the poor old thing waiting till midnight." "*Faugh!* Bally black savages, the lot of them! You give him a packet of chips an' a few cigarettes an' he'll be happy as a king! To hell with Barbara Castle!"

I looked to Pierre without hope. Pierre looked back dully, then, almost imperceptibly, his eyes dilated. Had he been appearing in a comic strip a cloud labelled "idea" would have risen, attached by a slender filament to his head. "Bert, I'm awfully sorry," he said, "but much as we'd love to . . . er, to join you and Dolly, we really won't be able to. I can't think how I could have forgotten about it, but I've just remembered now that Burkitt asked me to call in at the Ruwalo police camp on our return to collect a rather important docket from the sub-inspector there. I can hardly keep a senior officer up till past midnight while I indulge in a licentious orgy in town. Awfully sorry, but there it is. Duty comes first, and all that."

The pretext was both indisputable and convincing and was glumly accepted. Pierre and I had both been unnerved by Bert's exultant opposition to all our former pleas. Now that the danger had passed our spirits revived. We were able to lament the loss of an evening's entertainment with such gravity and despondence that Bert's own dejection lessened. He rallied us with a proposal of beating up the town with him on some future occasion when duty could not intervene. The possibility cheered us all and he parted from us in the best of humours with a jubilant promise that the Coq d'Or would see us yet.

\* \* \*

We bought the dish-cloths, then drifted about the china and hardware department, scoffing at the monstrous china ornaments and disconcerting the unctuous shop assistants. We failed to see Betty Harker till she bore down upon us with cries of delight.

"Fancy finding *you* here!" she said, "*Everyone* seems to be in town today. I've just been talking to Brenda Fawcett in the ladies' powder room, and before that I met Belinda and Irma buying chocolates for little Angela. It's such fun meeting friends in town like this! Though of course I always say the population is so small that one only needs to come in often enough to recognise a host of familiar strangers. Now what have you two been buying? Show me everything!" We explained that our purchases were as yet limited to dish-cloths.

"But of course! I know just how it is. One tramps the town for hours, and nothing to show for it! I've had the most frightful day looking for socks for Basil; he's so particular you know. Now I'm going to spend a little something on myself at last. I need a new evening gown for the party at the Ellis-Parkers'. I rather want something in midnight blue. Quite plain, of course. No frills. A draped effect perhaps, with a little marcasite brooch at the shoulder. Brenda has just been telling me about the flame-coloured frock she's bought. I couldn't tell her so, of course, but it sounded *quite* unsuitable! Plump women should stick to black. But then, of course, poor Brenda wants to go gay, to use her own words. I rather suspect she hopes to cut a dash with that charming young man, Oliver Lindsay. I expect I'm quite wrong, I certainly hope so for poor Michael's sake, but she did seem to be a little enamoured of Oliver at the gymkhana. But I've no doubt she'll look quite fetching. However, I expect Oliver will be occupied with Belinda. From what Belinda said when I saw her, I gather she imagines Oliver will ask her to be his partner at the dance. She seemed very excited and had bought herself a new necklace. She would be quite pretty if only her eyebrows weren't so shaggy and her complexion were not so blotchy. But I'm sure she'll look quite sweet all the same."

As we had little to relate and nothing to show her, Mrs Harker did not detain us long. We watched the retreating thrust of her relentless shoulders, so soon to be draped in midnight blue.

At the end of the day our legs were weary and our spirits torpid from the surfeit of merchandise that was paraded with self-applause in every window. Our consciences were oppressed by the ceaseless, submissive procession of humans who passed with so little buoyancy in their step and so little animation in their eyes. Woman shoppers have a film over their eyes, a look of hypnotic concentration; their legs move with a mechanical energy; their cheeks quiver with each jarring step; and their chins lead the way in urgent advance of their bodies.

Alighting from the pavement in front of us was a familiar figure, that of Brenda Fawcett. She turned at our greeting and smiled limpidly over her rustling parcels.

" Hello! You been shopping, too? Isn't it frantic? I feel I could drop. I find everything takes so *long*. The shop girls are *so* dim-witted when you're trying to find the right thing, and then of course they're so painfully *zealous* when they're trying to sell you something you don't want at all. I haven't even come to the end of my list *yet*. Halfway through, when I felt a complete wreck, I collapsed in a powder room to restore my ravaged appearance and in sailed Betty Harker. There was I, drooping under a mountain of parcels and attempting to apply lipstick with a shaking hand, and incidentally smudging it, and Betty firing questions at me till my head reeled. Garrulous isn't the word. And the curiosity! She all but started unwrapping my parcels to see what was inside them. Can you believe it, she's determined on midnight blue with drapes for the party? With her *size*! What with Belinda Storm tossing about in pink like a piece of Turkish delight and Betty posing as the dowager *femme fatale*, I fear you and I must accept the lesser rôle of the demure wallflowers, Carol. Well, I must go and set poor Michael's mind at rest. He's been soaking up cocktails at the Dolphin for the past hour and probably quite resigned himself to the certainty of my having been carried off squealing by some ardent admirer!"

At sunset we sank into the car with the glad feeling of escape. We drove past the Rhodes National Art Gallery with its extended lines of uncluttered simplicity. We turned into Kingsway, passed the venerable parade of mellow, tousle-headed palms, and were once again engulfed in the cacophony of the Cow's Guts.

Langton was nowhere to be seen. By unwonted good fortune we secured a parking space and sat watching the constant stream of people and traffic.

Though clothes-conscious, the Africans do not adopt a new fashion every season; and seemingly less prone to differences in temperature, their apparel is not restricted by climatic conditions. Should a piccanin possess a coat— some voluminous cast-off that has clad a more exacting and less deserving figure in former days—he will keep it proudly wrapped about his person throughout a melting summer.

Despite the ubiquitous announcements of greatly reduced prices a pair of men's shoes that featured in the motley amassment of a bargain sale were marked at forty-five shillings, and a great many garden boys draw a monthly wage of three pounds. But the African disposes of his entire earnings with little hesitation. The urge to hoard is uncommon; the future is remote and caution pointless. And the African does not hesitate to turn this open-handedness of his brothers to his own account. There are a considerable number of African bus owners who provide transport for their African clients in the country at a high cost. Such a figure operated near Dzokuti and, without arousing any resentment, bought himself a large American car from the fares of his less fortunate kin.

"Let's drive round the block," suggested Pierre after we had waited in vain for Langton to appear, "Perhaps he's confused the corners."

We had scarcely drawn away from the corner when an agonised wail caused us to look back. Heedless of the vehicles that hooted in warning and swerved to avoid him, Langton hurried unsteadily down the street waving in one hand a new hat and in the other a new black saucepan.

"*Mambo!* Mambo, Mambo, *Mambo!*" He fell into the car with incoherent and very nearly tearful reproaches. "I'm think you go leaving me here by Sosbry! Eeee! Mambo!" The strong, sour odour of native beer became an almost palpable presence in the car. As we negotiated Salisbury's homebound traffic, Langton felt it necessary to give us a brief résumé of his activities. But his memory was confused and all he could give us was a vague recollection of being photographed in a booth for five shillings, and a candid avouchment for the potency of location beer.

"But why should you be afraid that we'd leave you in Salisbury?" said Pierre patiently, "How could we go back to Dzokuti without a cook boy?"

"I'm think maybe sometime you go find 'nother boy," said Langton with the facile logic of the simple mind. His anxiety was of short duration, however, for before we had left the precincts of the city his saucepan and brown trilby had rolled to the floor of the car and Langton was sound asleep.

## CHAPTER ELEVEN

A DUIKER stepped delicately between the lettuce rows in the Ellis-Parkers' vegetable garden, undisturbed by the shrill laughter and the rhythm of drum and clarinet that throbbed and wailed across the wakeful, moonlit bush.

Because he had no car of his own, we had arranged to take Derek Vaughn to the dance, while the Burkitts had offered to take him home. And because of his sensitivity to what he termed "the feel of the thing" we had made no haste to enter into the gaiety of the Ellis-Parkers' balloon-decked tobacco-grading shed before ten o'clock in the evening. "A party has inevitably three phases and one must never arrive before the termination of the first," explained Derek, "The first phase being *andante*—everyone hesitant

and a little dubious as to the outcome; the second *allegro*—
everyone desperately jolly; the third of course *adagio*—
everyone feels that everyone else is looking rather tawdry."

Chromium embellishments on countless cars gleamed in
the moonlight and we edged our small Anglia past a succession of vehicles of extraordinary length, each of which
boasted what America calls wings but are in fact more like
deformed scapulae, projecting aggressively into the drive.
Baby-sitters in the country are scarce and children cannot be
left on an isolated farm, particularly on a Saturday night
when kaffir beer has been brewed in the compound. Our
progress to the grading shed was therefore observed by a
great many wide-eyed children. Their pale, pudgy faces,
some ovoid and some spherical, bobbed about inside the
parked cars and were pressed to the windows between extended fingers. If we peered at them in their rumpled blankets, the little faces grimaced or remained passive, depending upon their age and disposition, but all stared back with
that crafty innocence peculiar to children.

A dim light spread beyond the wide grading-shed doors
and we found on entering the shed that it was illumined with
scores of flickering candles. They were fastened to the walls
with home-made wire brackets. Though Jennifer's pre-
diction that I should be called upon to impale millions
of cocktail sausages on toothpicks had not come to pass,
it was evident that someone had been called upon to
impale a great many candles on wires. I remarked upon
the fact to Derek, who drawled that someone else had
been called upon to blow up millions of blue and green
balloons.

"Betty Harker has shown surprising artistry, nevertheless," he said, "The agitated light of the candles and the
blue and green balloons swaying overhead give a sort of

ocean-bed effect. There are a number of rather red-faced
gentlemen at the far end of the room who are already
drinking like fishes and thereby enhancing the marine-like
appearance of the whole thing."

Though the dance was held on the premises of the Ellis-
Parkers, they were not expected to act as host and hostess,
for the party was a communal enterprise. As we stood
somewhat hesitantly in the doorway, an elderly couple
danced jerkily past us wearing coloured paper hats. Pierre
told me that they were the Ellis-Parkers. Mr Ellis-Parker
was whistling piercingly through his teeth. When we had
grown accustomed to the deep-sea light, we distinguished
people from the Dzokuti district. We recognised Oliver
Lindsay's employer, Jimmy Wright, sipping a drink in a
corner. His Adam's apple bobbed actively and he did not
look at all jolly. We overheard Mrs Wright say to a group
of people near us: "Jimmy's in one of his ugly moods. He
hates wearing a collar and tie, he almost never does . . . he
gets these ugly moods." His sunburnt, turtle-like neck
certainly did look rather constricted.

"I must escape!" said Derek suddenly. "A freakish
Amazon in white is hurtling towards us." The woman in
white was Belinda Storm. The innocuous frills with which
she had formerly enhanced her maidenly bloom had been
renounced. Tonight she was tightly swathed in alluring
white satin. A considerable amount of her pink back was
daringly exposed and vied in interest with the size of the
vaccination disks on the upper half of her arm. She bounded
towards us, "Hullo! Hullo! Hullo! I've just been trying to
rock and roll with someone called Bert Goldman! Oooph!
I'm out of breath. I thought I saw Derek with you but he
seems to have vanished like the Invisible Man!" She
laughed exuberantly.

"I think he went to find a drink," said Pierre. "I was

just about to get something for Carol; could I bring you one, too?"

"Oh, please. I need a pick-me-up! I think there's orange-ade. Or else ginger ale."

Pierre was absorbed into the mass and Belinda stayed beside me regaining her breath. "I'm terribly out of train-ing," she said. "I used to be able to leap about for absolute ages without getting the least bit puffed. I taught gymnastics at Gaggleswithian's, you know."

"Oh, that must have been interesting," I said, while my attention was held by a sharp skirmish between the Dutoits. John was moving with determination to the refreshment table with an empty glass in his hand, and Irma endeavoured with matching determination to manœuvre her husband toward the dance floor.

"Oh, you can't imagine what joy it gave me," said Belinda, "to see those girls responding . . . they really loved their gym classes. Some of them were a bit backward at first. I remember one girl in particular, Venetia Dauncey-Chalmers was her name. She didn't want to get thick ankles. But we soon had her climbing the ribs and bars like a monkey You can't imagine the satisfaction of it."

Oliver Lindsay foxtrotted by with Brenda Fawcett. Oliver's head was bent at an attentive angle and Brenda's drooped in an attitude of helpless submission. The sparkle left Belinda's eyes and though she continued to recall her days at Gaggleswithian's she recalled them with less satis-faction. Presently she ceased to recall them at all. She gazed at the dancers with a look of blind intensity. It was disap-pointing because she had abandoned Venetia Dauncey-Chalmers at an exciting stage in the girl's gymnastic pro-gress.

"Let's find Pierre and those drinks," I said and drew her forcibly away. We found Pierre with Derek. Observing

Belinda's stricken look, Derek asked her with a deep sigh and an outrageous show of reluctance to dance with him; he pushed her backwards with a quick-step that in no way coincided with the tempo of the music. Belinda was thus safely removed from the scene when a few moments later Brenda and Oliver arrived with an inordinate amount of laughter, panting and raillery. Brenda fanned her flushed face with a handkerchief. "Whatever you do, don't dance with this man!" she cried, one hand resting possessively on Oliver's sleeve, "He scarcely looks where he's going and pays one the most *scandalous* compliments the whole time. I simply won't have anything more to do with him! Oliver, be a lamb and mix me a gin swizzle, will you?" She turned to us again, "I feel *madly* gay tonight! It's like the dear old Bahamas all over again, fighting to keep the males at bay. You enjoying yourself Carol? You look rather bored. Or just plain thirsty! I must say I'm simply dying for that gin. . . . I do wish Maurice were here. He danced the tango so divinely; only Frenchmen really know how to dance a tango. I wonder if I dare ask the band to give us one. You must allow Pierre to have just one tango with me, Carol. I feel Oliver will be too, too utterly English about it. Poor Oliver, though, I mustn't make him jealous!" Brenda's gin swizzle was quickly disposed of and as they whirled away once more Oliver's eyebrows quivered and Brenda sang "I could have danced all night" in a high, trilling warble.

"Watching Brenda, I feel we can no longer possibly be described as Newly Weds," said Pierre. "We make a very staid old married couple. Shall we take the floor in a dignified manner?" While we danced, Pierre talked softly to himself and eventually said that he had composed a little verse entitled The Three Graces. "It goes like this," he said :

"Betty, Brenda and solid Belinda,
One will triumph—two will hinder.
Belinda, Betty and such a gay Brenda,
All arrayed in seductive splendour.
Brenda, Belinda and dowager Betty—
Devoted to Oliver—which one'll *get he*?"

The floor was very crowded and strange feet, elbows and shoulders constantly caught the heels of my shoes, hit me in the small of the back or brushed the top of my head. The owners of the joints and extremities commented upon these encounters in a variety of ways. There were those who said in embarrassment: "Oh I say, I'm most *frightfully* sorry, did I hurt you?" There were some who called cheerily: "Look where you're going, chum!" There were others, more surly, who asked Pierre if he thought he owned the bloody floor. And there were those who made no comment at all and merely shuffled past us with baleful glares and animal grunts. A communal country dance provides a mixed bag. I could not echo Brenda's song and after a time we swam out of the turgid river of dancers and hauled ourselves up the bank to the edge of the room in some relief.

Derek Vaughn appeared beside us with a wicked smile and told us that he had lost Belinda to a hefty farmer. "I haven't the courage to worm myself and worse still to steer a wench through all that again," he said, "and besides, my feet have been irreparably damaged, and I did rather value my feet—they were so *useful*." He leant in a drooping curve against the wall. "Far better to savour the rich spectacle of humans at play. Look, for instance, at that large and energetic personage in midnight blue—I refer to Mrs Harker. One would have thought that the exhaustive amount of effort she put into decorating the ballroom and organising this whole affair would have been sufficient to incapacitate her for the remainder of the evening. But no! Her organising abilities are limitless. Oliver outwitted her at the beginning of the evening by sheltering behind the buoyant Brenda, but though she has been temporarily foiled she is biding her time in a very charitable manner. She is in fact *organising the wallflowers*. Do look!" We looked and saw Betty Harker striding across one end of the room. When she reached the unsuspecting Jimmy Wright, she laid a hand on his shoulder and, as he flinched, disarmed him with her intimate smile. We were unable to hear what she said to him, but it seemed to be in the nature of an appeal which Jimmy, caught unawares, found impossible to reject. She came sweeping back with Jimmy stumbling after her, his Adam's apple leaping. She halted before Mrs Fanshawe who was talking to a robust woman in emerald green. "There now," cried Betty Harker, "no more excuses about no one wanting to dance with you, Jimmy Wright! You men all seem to think parties are only arranged so that you can talk farming with your cronies. We women come to *dance*!" Mrs Fanshawe turned with a look of astonishment and was immediately clasped in Jimmy's arms. He looked astonished himself, as he whisked her stiffly away. "Well, I never!" said the robust woman. But Mrs Harker was already out of earshot. She had spied Jimmy Wright's timorous spouse. "Now this is all nonsense, my dear!" we heard her boom, "We can't have you hiding yourself like this; it won't do at all! There's dear Mr Fanshawe all by himself with no one to talk to. Come along. I'm sure he'd like to dance with you." Twittering and protesting, Mrs Wright was hustled forward and all but precipitated into the arms of the startled Native Commissioner. Mr Fanshawe quickly recovered his poise. "My dear Mrs Wright, believe me I should have asked you long ago but I'm afraid my steps are shockingly old-fashioned; dancing seems so very reckless nowadays. If you'd care to take the risk?"

Betty Harker left them with a gratified smile. She hesitated and looked about her. Irma Dutoit stood alone near the refreshment table, nibbling salted nuts from a bowl. The nuts appeared to taste extremely bitter, though she persisted in sampling them. Betty's eyes gleamed at this solitary figure. She hurried off towards another man who stood with hunched shoulders on the outskirts of a group of farmers. She tapped him on the back. "Now why is this naughty man standing about when I can see a charming young woman who is simply dying to dance with him?" The naughty man turned. He was Irma Dutoit's husband and he looked very indignant. "Oh!" said Betty, but she was undeterred. "Now, John, we can't have this sort of thing, you know!"

" Well who's dying to dance with me?" said John.

" Oh . . . why Mrs Putters-Brooke is."

"Then tell the old trout I don't want to dance with her." John turned his back again and Betty Harker was forced to withdraw. "You see how fascinating it all is," murmured Derek, "and you have such contrasts in the way people approach the thing. Take the Barnetts for example. Just before you came Veronica floated past in the arms of Billy Burkitt and when she saw me she called out ' Rather fun, isn't it?' A moment later Grahame Barnett danced by. He wielded the stout Mrs Monksfoote, who ignored him completely. She was carrying on a conversation with some other elderly lady across the room, which gave him the opportunity of mumbling at me as they passed. He said, 'Great Scott! Isn't everything too utterly grim!' All very significant. I mean it does so emphasise the fact that life is what one makes it."

"Oh Lord!" said Pierre, "There's poor old Belinda deserted again. I'll have to ask her to dance." Pierre looked sufficiently eager about his request to cause Belinda a little confusion. She had been munching salted almonds, and when she saw him approaching she tossed an almond up to her mouth with a display of nonchalance. Unfortunately the effect was lost because the almond fell before it reached her lips, and worse, it fell inside the bodice of her dress. "Really, one might think she was nursing a viper in her bosom," drawled Derek with amusement, for Belinda's covert attempts to retrieve the nut became increasingly frantic as Pierre drew nearer. "I should leave it," said Pierre briefly and Belinda responded with hysterical laughter. "Oh, it *tickles*!" she snorted.

Derek was in the midst of reporting the movements of Brenda Fawcett who was dancing, he told me in amazement, with Dr Brodie, when Oliver Lindsay appeared before us. He bowed low. "I do hope Derek will forgive my intrusion," he said. "I come in the hopes that you will trip the light fantastic with me, Carol?"

We waltzed for a time in silence. I waited hopefully for a scandalous compliment but none came. Not even a respectable one. His eyebrows were perfectly stationary and I felt rather dashed. But my confidence was restored when I realised from his subsequent remarks that even if he did not find me bewitchingly feminine there was a remote possibility that he regarded me as an intellectual.

"Odd the way one moment one can be quite fanatically rumbustious and superficial, as it were, and the next a sort of compassion for humanity as a whole lifts one above trivialities," he mused. "By achieving a balance between the two I've managed to evolve a sort of philosophy of life. One might say I've *come to terms with myself*."

"What are the terms?" I asked with a genuine interest. Oliver found them difficult to define. "One finds it impossible," he said, "to generalise over these things. One has to avoid the pitfalls of shallow thinking. One must form a definite code of existence and apply it to one's everyday life. . . ."

" What is one's . . . your code of existence?" I asked, my interest unabated. Between the buffetings we received from our fellow dancers I heard him murmur disjointedly on tranquillity of the mind, self-counsel, humanitarianism, and even something that sounded like oscillating counterpoise. He finally cleared his throat. "I live on the same principle as a yo-yo," he said gravely. "I think that sums it up pretty well. You know those wooden things on a long string. One keeps them constantly on the move. That's rule number one: never allow yourself to stagnate; one gives them full play on the string and they come shooting up again as if they were on an elastic thread. Rule two, you see: enjoy yourself to the hilt but don't break that elastic thread of self-discipline; jerk yourself back to the sober realities of Life."

"Or, one could say, stretch the self-discipline and plumb the depths," I said, "and you'll be jerked back willy-nilly by the law."

"Well, no. It's not quite the same thing," said Oliver seriously, "You see the whole exercise is voluntary."

Looking at the perpetual and seemingly aimless movement of over fifty people in the same direction, I was reminded of the disastrous migrations of the lemmings; that, coupled with a picture of Oliver rising and falling ceaselessly on his yo-yo of life, made me feel rather giddy. I was not distressed when a crescendo of drumbeats brought the waltz to an end, and the members of the dance band mopped their brows with their handkerchiefs and mingled with the crowd at the refreshment table.

Betty Harker's voice attracted us to a corner of the room where a gathering of people were dimly distinguishable through the smoke of their cigarettes. Betty was speaking with great warmth about a man called "Dear Frederick". Dear Frederick was such a naughty old recluse. He kept an aviary and fed the birds himself every day. "Such a delightful little insight on his essential character, I always think." When Betty told Colonel Putters-Brooke that Dear Frederick was the most unassuming man one could wish to meet I had an idea that Dear Frederick might be Lord Greaves. He was. "I first met him at Sir Hubert Tolemly's house in 1946," said Betty. She turned to Veronica Barnett. "It really is such a shame you and Grahame were away when he came out here," she said; "you would have *loved* him."

Basil Harker looked surprised, "But, dear, I thought you met him when you were organising that jumble sale at Sutton-upon-Derwent, or was it Burton-upon-Stather?"

"Don't be silly, Basil!" said Betty quickly. "And *what* are you doing with an empty glass in your hand? Go and pour yourself a nice strong whisky at once. I want to see everyone enjoying themselves!"

Brenda Fawcett blew a magnificent smoke-ring in Grahame Barnett's direction. "It *is* a pity you missed meeting Lord Greaves," she said. "He's really rather a poppet. Sort of *ancien rgéime*. . . ." Jennifer Burkitt agreed. "What I call a decent type of bloke," she said.

Presently Basil Harker rejoined us, somewhat hesitantly. His glass was once again empty and Betty told him to go and pour himself a nice gin and tonic. When he returned some time later he was breathing heavily and he grasped the back of a chair. He watched Betty fixedly while she talked; after several minutes she became aware of his presence and glanced at him. He beamed. "Hullo, love," he said, "C-c-c-c. C-c-c. C-couldn't we go? I feel q-q-q. . . ."

"Basil! I do believe you've had too much to drink! Really, Basil, how *could* you!" She turned to Mrs Monksfoote with a helpless shrug. "What can one do?" she said, "Of course, he never knows when to stop." She told Basil that he would simply have to go and sleep it off outside in their car. Basil left the grading-shed with slow and measured steps.

With the dismissal of her husband and the dispersal of the wallflowers, Betty Harker had tidied up all the loose ends, so to speak, and cleared the decks for action. She beckoned to Oliver Lindsay with a daintily hooked little finger. "Come along now, you lazy man, I've work for you," she cried. "It's high time we replaced all these candles or we'll be left in darkness. There's a big box of candles in a little store room round the back somewhere and I'd like you to come with me and fetch them."

"Delighted," said Oliver, and strode out with Betty, looking very manly and helpful.

The flames along the walls flickered lower; the light became increasingly dim and the irregularities of the cement floor caused many an awkward stumble, but Betty and Oliver did not return. The situation worsened and people murmured about the torches in their cars. Before any action was taken, however, Oliver made a sudden reappearance. There was an urgency about his entry, though he scarcely seemed to notice the cavern-like gloom with which we were surrounded, and he had not brought any candles. He hurried away to the end of the room and poured himself a drink. When Betty Harker arrived soon afterwards, she carried the box of candles herself. She gave Oliver a look full of bitter scorn, set the box on the floor with a thump and began distributing candles in a silence which gave her helpers no inducement to chatter.

Derek, who followed events with the lynx-eyed sedulity

of a society reporter, told us some ten minutes later that
Oliver had been persuaded to brave the dark once more.
Belinda had taken him outside with her on the pretext of
making sure that little Angy was comfortably asleep in the
Dutoits' car. "Having been, as it were, unnerved by the
dowager, he hopes to recover his grip with the damosel,"
said Derek, "but the softly blooming damosel has still to
contend with the polish and wit of the young matron.
Brenda has arranged herself to the best possible advantage
under one of the newly-lit candles and awaits their return
with a slightly distraught air. She reminds me of that
Victorian painting entitled 'He Cometh Not'."

Innumerable insects were attracted by the light above
Brenda's head and she suffered their buzzings and dronings
with fortitude. Michael Fawcett stood in attendance, dis-
entangling moths from her hair and stamping on the beetles
that ran derisively over her feet. I felt a certain womanly
sympathy for her and went to join in the massacre of the
insects. Unfortunately a very large horned beetle settled on
my neck and Michael forgot all else in his determination to
secure so immense a trophy.

Brenda credited the beetle with a Cupid cunning. In her
view it had alighted on me in a deliberate attempt to draw
her husband to my side. "Really, Michael!" she said,
flapping her hands peevishly at an exquisite apple-green
moth, "one might call that 'approach number one'. I
wonder if Carol will fall for such a simple stratagem!"
Michael's true intentions were never discovered, for the
bettle lifted its gleaming wings and zoomed out beyond the
open door into the starlit sky. Belinda and Oliver came in at
the same time that the beetle went out, but the animated
manner which Brenda assumed as soon as they entered was
of no avail. Oliver guided Belinda tenderly toward the
dancers and only tantalising glimpses could be had of them,

weaving and bobbing between the throng. A momentary view of Belinda's upturned face brought to my mind two lines from 'The Eve of St. Agnes' by Keats which tell of the young virgin, Madeline, tripping through a scene of revelry and brooding on love:

"She danc'd along with vague, regardless eyes,
Anxious her lips, her breathing quick and short. . . ."
The resemblance was striking and I was so intrigued with Belinda's vague, regardless eyes that Brenda's departure went unnoticed. "She's gone home in a huff," drawled Derek delightedly. "Someone will have to give Michael a lift when the party breaks up, because she went in their car."

Michael seemed quite unperturbed. He came across to us with a bland smile and remarked that the party was in need of a stimulant. "I shall have to mix some Bahama punch," he said, "a little speciality of mine that never fails, and we do rather need it. I mean, really, look at John and Irma Dutoit. They're exactly like a pair of sheep bleating about on a fog-bound moor. . . . Jimmy Wright looks like a weary old crow that's been kept too long in captivity. And then we have the commanding but somehow dejected figure of our noble Fanshawe."

"I still have a vivid picture of our noble Fanshawe strongly reacting to what one might call one of nature's stimulants," said Derek, stroking his chin with his delicate hand. "Do you remember, Michael, the scorpion episode?" Michael gave a shout of laughter. "I do, indeed! We must tell Carol and Pierre about that. First of all I should explain that Fanshawe was in the habit of retiring to the office lavatory during working hours for prolonged periods. He was invariably equipped with an armful of Government Gazettes, reports, letters and other documents requiring his attention. One morning Derek and I found a large black scorpion outside the courtroom and, acting on some devilish impulse, we caught it in a cigarette box—it was a remarkably *sluggish* sort of scorpion, wasn't it, Derek?—and released it on the lavatory seat. Not long afterwards old Fanshawe trotted off with the usual bundle of papers under his arm. Quite a prodigious stack of reading matter he took that morning, but it was all back on his desk again in a trice. Some of the gazettes fell by the wayside and weren't retrieved till the following day."

Both Derek and Michael, still chuckling reminiscently, were somewhat disconcerted when Mr Fanshawe himself appeared in our midst. However, Mr Fanshawe wore his smile with a broadness and fixity that were certain to put everyone at ease. "Aha!" he said, "May I be let in on the little joke? Or is it a little too *risqué* for an old sermoniser like myself?"

"Well, yes. I think perhaps it is a little too *risqué*," said Derek slowly. With the arrival of Mr Fanshawe conversation became more general. The dangers of African nationalism and of African agitators fed on Cairo propaganda were discussed.

"I must say I sympathised with Lord Greaves when he said he was sick of the problems of the White Settlers and the Blacks. But the pity of it is that people simply won't get down to the core of the matter," Mr Fanshawe said impressively; "the core tends to be rather indigestible, I suppose, and they prefer to nibble round the cortex—at least I believe that is the botanical term."

Derek was not to be outdone in simile. "The White Settlers and the Blacks are rather like chessmen," he said. "I feel the White Settlers would be the pawns, moving in one step at a time; the Blacks would be the knights, because they feel that the best way to deal with the obstacle of civilisation is to take an oblique leap over it. . . . Though, of course, to have your knights outnumbering your pawns would necessitate a new set of rules for the game. . . ." But most of us had already transferred our attention to the higher pitched voice of Freda Harris. "My dears, have you read this new novel everyone's talking about?" she asked. "It gets in a wonderful dig against something—I forget just what." Annoyed with this want of perception in his listeners, Derek murmured behind me that the party had obviously approached the *adagio* stage. "A party can be diverting, but it reaches a point when the whole masquerade becomes wearisome," he yawned. "Pungent witticisms become facetious badinage and the *drôleries* of our friends lose their appeal. If anyone asked me what I thought was the nicest thing about a party, I'd say the certainty of the bed waiting for one at home, when all our little conventionalities and vaporous bluffs can be peeled off with our clothes. Pillows and sheets are so uncritical."

Michael Fawcett mixed the Bahama rum punch and people were affected in various ways. Dr Brodie became unexpectedly frolicsome and pursued Betty Harker round the refreshment table. John Dutoit won his wife's approval by calling Betty Harker a silly sausage in a very loud voice, and then incurred his wife's wrath by applying a lighted match to every balloon within his reach. Irma tightened her lips and told her husband to stop fooling about like a schoolboy. When, like a schoolboy, he disobeyed, she told Belinda that it was high time they took little Angy home and put her in a decent bed. Belinda was unresponsive.

"Well, if you wish to gawp at Mr Lindsay for the rest of the night, you may do so!" said Irma, snatching up her bag, and her evening coat, which was black with purple sequins spattered across the shoulders. Little Angela must have made a very bumpy journey home for, when she left, her mother was in no mood to trifle with potholes and corrugations.

Apart from the odd muffled whoop, Bert Goldman had been strangely quiet all the evening. The rum punch renewed his spirit, however, and, after gaining the attention of as many people as he could by distorting his face with a series of exaggerated winks and making incomprehensible signs with his huge fingers behind his back, he sidled past Mrs Fanshawe and as he did so—to use his own expression—he 'pinched her bottom'. Bert clearly found her reaction disappointing. She took half a step forward with a barely perceptible frown and continued to talk to Mrs Putters-Brooke about an exhibition of needlework that was to be held in Salisbury.

Veronica Barnett was affected by the rum punch in much the same way as a young schoolgirl might be affected after two glasses of sherry: everything became terribly funny. "You should write a book about all this," she giggled, making a vague gesture with her hand. She giggled again. "I know Grahame and I would find ourselves in it under some flimsy disguise. What fun! All my little nonsenses said in my more unguarded moments. . . ."

Mr Fanshawe drank a quantity of the punch and became effusive and just a little maudlin. His eyes passed over the interior of the grading shed and its inhabitants with an expression of warm affection and after a time he stood up and raised his glass. "I propose a vote of thanks to Bet . . . to Mrs Harker," he said, breathing hard. "Without fear of coradiction I may say that if it weren't for Mrs Harker we wouldn't be enjoying dance t'night. Trem'dous 'mount of work. I take my head off to her, I really do." Mr Fanshawe sat down heavily. There were a few seconds of silence and then a crackling volley of handclaps. Chins were lifted and necks stretched in an effort to discover the whereabouts of Betty Harker and to see how she was affected by this tribute. When Mrs Harker was found to be perched on

Dr Brodie's knee in a corner of the room and appeared not to have heard the tribute at all, our clapping ceased and, with the exception of Bert Goldman who whistled, we all pretended we had not seen her. "Let's Pretend" is a game of enchantment with children and a game of necessity with adults.

In an opposite corner of the grading shed Belinda had settled on Oliver's knee. An inch of ash trembled from the tip of Oliver's cigarette and Belinda tickled his ear.

Derek still brooded on the white man's future in Africa and, becoming increasingly downcast, deplored the flippant unconcern of those about him. "Our eviction is inevitable. . . . I see it now. Yet look at these poor clowns. One might call the whole scene 'Colonial Attitudes before the Bust-up' . . . ." He sighed.

Pierre and I decided to leave when melting wax hung in stalactites from the wire candle holders and slowly dribbled on to the floor. Praying mantises circled the dwindling flames, sizzled their wings, and fell among the weakly struggling mass of insects whose thread-like legs trailed over the glossy hummocks of candle grease that lay below. There was something symbolic in their hopeless scrambling. The remaining people circled the refreshment table, which was littered with sticky-rimmed, finger-printed tumblers, and flopped weakly into chairs, trailing their tired legs. Undoubtedly there was a similarity.

Yet the end of a party sees people at their most natural; affections are dissolved in fatigue; death is the great leveller, but exhaustion also smoothes a good many social humps and swellings. If we are at our most human towards the end of a party, are insects, I wondered, at their most insect—moths at their most mothlike and beetles at their most beetle?

Along the road that led us home nightjars squatted at

intervals, reluctant to rise, fixing us with brilliant yellow eyes. Rabbits were less daring and a succession of little lop-eared bundles raced desperately and unswervingly down the broad beam of our headlamps.

Coming over the last hill, we dazzled Betty Harker's diminutive Pekingese with our lights. He sat beside the petrol pumps, his mouth primly pursed, his button eyes gleaming with hostility . . . or was it self-satisfaction?

When we fumbled a way into our unlit cottage, the topaz African moon had long since retired; Orion had keeled over; and frogs sang a ballad of love in the dark.